Verbal Reasoning

10 Minute Tests

8–9 years

TEST 1: **Similars and Opposites**

Test time: 0 — 5 — 10 minutes

Underline the pair of words most similar in meaning.

Example   come, go   <u>roam, wander</u>   fear, fare

1. book, word   story, tale   letter, pen
2. sight, vision   expect, delay   common, unusual
3. caught, loose   criminal, prison   free, release
4. cheese, biscuits   dish, bowl   bread, jam
5. stop, go   finish, halt   begin, end

Underline the two words, one from each group, which are most opposite in meaning.

Example   (dawn, <u>early</u>, wake)   (<u>late</u>, stop, sunrise)

6. (sensible, sense, every)   (feel, foolish, all)
7. (section, piece, war)   (peace, portion, argue)
8. (heavy, handsome, pale)   (pretty, eager, light)
9. (ripe, rise, steer)   (ready, guide, fall)
10. (mine, major, below)   (ours, minor, under)

Underline the word in the brackets closest in meaning to the word in capitals.

Example   UNHAPPY   (unkind   death   laughter   <u>sad</u>   friendly)

11. LIE   (down   sleep   bed   fib   truth)
12. CATCH   (escape   throw   capture   chase   ball)
13. WOMAN   (child   male   daughter   lady   man)
14. COMBINE   (harvest   divide   blend   separate   keep)
15. CHARGE   (attack   loss   change   guard   coin)

Total

TEST 2: Sorting Words

Test time: 0 5 10 minutes

Rearrange the muddled letters in capitals to make a proper word. The answer will complete the sentence sensibly.

Example   A BEZAR is an animal with stripes.   __ZEBRA__

1 On November 5th, we are going to a IEOKRWFR display. _____
2 Last Saturday and DYANUS, it rained all day. _____
3 Over the summer, our lawn needed constant WMNIOG. _____
4 Please be TUQEI and finish your work. _____
5 Toby painted a beautiful CTPIREU. _____

Look at these groups of words.

GROUP A: COUNTIES   GROUP B: PLANETS

Choose the correct group for each of the following words. Write in the letter.

6 Kent   _____
7 Saturn   _____
8 Venus   _____
9 Durham   _____
10 Mars   _____

Underline the two words which are the odd ones out in the following groups of words.

Example   black   <u>king</u>   purple   green   <u>house</u>

11	difficult	hard	complex	simple	easy
12	horse	shoe	sandal	wood	boot
13	clock	watch	observe	look	sea
14	scarlet	brown	red	maroon	black
15	huge	immense	tiny	little	large

Test 3: Selecting Letters

Find the letter which will end the first word and start the second word.

Example   peac (h) ome

1 val (__) ach
2 lam (__) ook
3 hal (__) ish
4 jaz (__) one
5 car (__) cho

Add one letter to the word given in capital letters to make a new word. The meaning of the new word is given in the clue.

Example   PLAN   simple   ___plain___

6   BUS   broken   _____
7   LOG   lengthy   _____
8   FAIL   delicate   _____
9   PINT   apply colour   _____
10 FLAT   opposite of sink _____

Remove one letter from the word in capitals to leave a new word. The meaning of the new word is given in the clue.

Example   AUNT   an insect   ___ant___

11 WIND   come first   _____
12 WHEAT   warmth   _____
13 CRANE   a walking stick   _____
14 BLEACH seashore   _____
15 FLIGHT not heavy   _____

Test 4: Selecting Words

Test time: 0 — 5 — 10 minutes

Underline two words, one from each group, that go together to form a new word. The word in the first group always comes first.

Example   (hand, <u>green</u>, for)   (light, <u>house</u>, sure)

1 (fore, hand, right)   (head, fit, sore)   2 (off, chatter, back)   (climb, box, on)
3 (best, high, kind)   (light, friend, nest) 4 (sock, wait, mush)   (or, foot, room)
5 (way, up, stand)   (ran, set, at)

Complete the following sentences by selecting the most sensible word from each group of words given in the brackets. Underline the words selected.

Example   The (<u>children</u>, books, foxes) carried the (houses, <u>books</u>, steps) home from the (greengrocer, <u>library</u>, factory).

6 Every (hair, night, holiday) before you go to (bed, London, school) you must brush your (dogs, teeth, cars).

7 Danielle's (coat, hill, garden) is (blue, wild, steep) with (red, winding, frightened) buttons.

8 The (frightened, hungry, loud) (dog, girl, balloon) gnawed on his (thumb, bone, firework).

9 The (pretty, clean, rusty) hinge on the garden (flower, gate, post) (squeaked, spoke, cycled) loudly.

10 Yesterday it (shone, rained, flew) heavily and there were (tall, deep, sunny) puddles all over the (sky, playground, pond).

Choose the word or phrase that makes each sentence true.

Example   A LIBRARY always has (posters, carpets, <u>books</u>, DVDs, stairs).

11 A LAKE always has (ducks, a view, water, boats, fish).
12 A LAWN always has (grass, a path, chairs, daisies, a pond).
13 A DOG always has a (collar, master, dinner, face, bone).
14 A MAIN ROAD always has (cars, tarmac, yellow lines, puddles, pavements).
15 A DUSTBIN always has (rubbish, rats, sides, bottles, cardboard).

Total

TEST 5: **Finding Words**

Test time: 0 — 5 — 10 minutes

Find the three-letter word which can be added to the letters in capitals to make a new word. The new word will complete the sentence sensibly.

Example   The cat sprang onto the MO.   __USE__

1 The little boy cried when his BOON popped.   _____

2 Mohammed likes bright colours like red and OGE.   _____

3 Our hockey M is unbeaten so far this season.   _____

4 Their GAR has a big lawn and a pond.   _____

5 Our family likes to play on the SGS and slides in the park.   _____

Write the four-letter word hidden at the end of one word and the beginning of the next word. The order of the letters may not be changed.

Example   The children had bats <u>and</u> balls.   __sand__

6 Please attach the labels to your jackets.   _____

7 The match is hanging in the balance.   _____

8 It is a good thing we are firm friends.   _____

9 My sister makes me tidy my room.   _____

10 Cutting my finger made me cry.   _____

Underline the one word which **cannot** be made from the letters of the word in capital letters.

Example   STATIONERY   stones   tyres   ration   <u>nation</u>   noisy

11 CANDLES   snail   scale   dance   clean   lance

12 BASKETS   skate   state   tasks   steak   bakes

13 FEATHER   there   father   heart   thief   three

14 CLAMBER   crawl   cream   blame   brace   clear

15 TREACLE   crate   trace   trees   clear   react

6

Total

Test 6: Alphabetical Order and Substitution

A B C D E F G H I J K L M N O P Q R S T U V W X Y Z

If these words were placed in alphabetical order, which word would come first? Underline the correct answer. The alphabet has been written out to help you.

1	brown	yellow	orange	white	purple
2	thigh	foot	chest	head	shoulder
3	July	August	September	October	November

In each line, underline the word which has its letters in alphabetical order.

4	petal	abbot	crime	tusks
5	salad	eight	flips	bossy
6	ghost	witch	moist	mouse
7	always	glory	stray	hover

Underline the word in each line which uses only letters from the first six letters of the alphabet.

8	baked	after	gladly	added
9	fable	guide	faced	caged
10	bead	ache	cats	fish

If a = 8, b = 2, c = 9 and d = 3, find the value of:

11 a + c + d = _____

12 2b + 2d = _____

13 3c – a = _____

14 (c – a) + d = _____

15 a + b + c + d = _____

TEST 7: **Word Progressions**

Test time: 0 — 5 — 10 minutes

Look at the first group of three words. The word in the middle has been made from the other two words. Complete the second group of three words in the same way, making a new word in the middle.

Example	PAIN	INTO	TOOK	ALSO	SOON	ONLY
1	BUSH	SHOP	OPEN	RUST	_____	IRON
2	CARS	CAPE	RIPE	PARK	_____	LESS
3	HORN	HOLE	LEAP	MOON	_____	REAL
4	CHIP	CAKE	WAKE	FLAN	_____	HIRE

Change the first word into the last word by changing one letter at a time and making a new, different word in the middle.

Example	CASE	CASH	LASH
5	TYRE	_____	FIRE
6	CASH	_____	CAKE
7	FORM	_____	FILM

Change the first word of the third pair in the same way as the other pairs to give a new word.

Example	bind, hind	bare, hare	but, hut
8	lamp, lump	sack, suck	care, _____
9	slow, glow	sale, gale	song, _____
10	first, fir	tinge, tin	hitch, _____
11	loaf, foal	team, meat	news, _____

Find the missing number by using the two numbers outside the brackets in the same way as the other sets of numbers.

Example	2 [8] 4	3 [18] 6	5 [25] 5
12	3 [4] 1	5 [7] 2	8 [__] 1
13	6 [5] 1	4 [1] 3	8 [__] 5
14	8 [11] 3	7 [12] 5	6 [__] 4
15	2 [6] 3	4 [8] 2	3 [__] 3

8

Total

TEST 8: Logic

Amy and Tom are wearing jeans.
Raj and Billie are wearing tracksuit bottoms.
Amy and Billie have blue tops.
Raj and Tom have green tops.

1. Who is wearing tracksuit bottoms and a blue top? _____
2. Is Raj wearing a green top and jeans? _____
3. What is Amy wearing with her blue top? _____

My bus should have arrived at 10:10. It is 15 minutes late.

4. What time is it now? _____

The bus waited at the bus stop for 5 minutes before leaving, and the journey took 20 minutes.

5. What time did I arrive at my destination? _____

The houses on one side of a street are even numbers from 2 to 20. On the other side they are odd numbers from 1 to 19. 1 is opposite 2, 3 is opposite 4 and so on. What number house is:

6. opposite 5? ___　　7. between 13 and 17? ___　　8. opposite 11? ___

Jake and Holly own football boots.
Jake and Sana have cricket boots.
Stuart and Holly own running shoes.
Sana and Stuart have tennis shoes.

9. Who has tennis shoes and cricket boots? _____
10. Who has running shoes and football boots? _____

A roasting joint weighs 2kg. It takes 45 minutes a kilogram to cook and must be done by 1pm. The potatoes will take 70 minutes and must be ready at the same time.

11–13　How long will the joint take to cook?　___ hr ___ mins
　　　　When should the food be put in the oven?　joint ___　potatoes ___

The day before yesterday was Wednesday. What is:

14. today? _____　　15. the day after tomorrow? _____

Time for a break! Go to Puzzle Page 42

Test 9: Codes

If the code for BEWARE is ZKPMHK, code and decode these words.

1. BEAR   _____
2. RAW   _____
3. BREW   _____
4. ZMHK   _____
5. PKMH   _____

Here are four number codes.
7619 4613 1993 9674
Match them to the words below and then work out the missing code.

6. HAND   _____
7. EACH   _____
8. CANE   _____
9. ACHE   _____
10. NEED   _____

Solve each question by working out the code.

11. If the code for TREAD is 67912, what is the code for DATE? _____
12. If the code for BEAST is FJODV, what is the code for BATS? _____
13. If the code for SLIME is BRPYX, what is the code for MILE? _____
14. If the code for PAINT is 35968, what is 3968? _____
15. If the code for THEME is $ + = * =, what is * = = $? _____

TEST 10: **Sequences**

Test time: 0 — 5 — 10 minutes

Complete the following sentences in the best way by choosing one word from each set of brackets.

Example Tall is to (tree, <u>short</u>, colour) as narrow is to (thin, white, <u>wide</u>).

1 Quick is to (slow, fast, clear) as dirty is to (close, far, clean).

2 Hat is to (scarf, head, warm) as glove is to (toes, hand, wool).

3 Three is to (four, seven, six) as five is to (ten, four, one).

4 Catch is to (ball, throw, draw) as rise is to (tall, follow, fall).

5 Go is to (depart, come, like) as small is to (little, round, far).

Fill in the missing letters and numbers.
The alphabet has been written out to help you.
A B C D E F G H I J K L M N O P Q R S T U V W X Y Z

Example AB is to CD as PQ is to <u>RS</u>.

6 PN is to LJ as HF is to _____.

7 16a is to 14b as 12c is to _____.

8 ABD is to EFH as IJL is to _____.

9 K1L is to M2N as O3P is to _____.

Give the missing pairs of letters in the following sequences.
The alphabet has been written out to help you.
A B C D E F G H I J K L M N O P Q R S T U V W X Y Z

Example CQ   DP   EQ   FP   GQ   <u>HP</u>

10 JK   LM   ____   PQ   RS   TU

11 FX   FW   ____   GU   GT   GS

12 ____ EG   IK   MO   QS   UW

Give the missing numbers in the following sequences.

Example 2   4   6   8   10   <u>12</u>

13 15   ____   23   27   31   35

14 21   18   15   ____   9   6

15 ____   4   8   16   32   64

11

Total

Test 11: Mixed

Rearrange the muddled letters in capitals to make a proper word. The answer will complete the sentence sensibly.

Example   A BEZAR is an animal with stripes.   ZEBRA

1 I have to go back to the STINTED for a filling.   _____
2 Soraya skilfully kicked the LLOBFATO.   _____
3 In the MERUSM holidays we are going to France.   _____
4 I like to watch the lambs GINYALP in the fields.   _____
5 Let's cross the road on the NALIPEC crossing.   _____

Underline the pair of words most opposite in meaning.

Example   cup, mug   coffee, milk   <u>hot, cold</u>

6   frost, snow   fresh, ripe   salty, sweet
7   even, equal   flexible, rigid   dark, shade
8   ghost, train   fail, pass   speak, talk
9   sensible, foolish crack, burst   rapid, fast
10 by, with   to, from   because, also

Solve each question by working out the code.

11 If the code for HOUSE is DRFPL, what is the code for SHOE?   _____
12 If the code for SHAME is 70832, what is the code for MESH?   _____
13 If the code for GREAT is DFMCV, what is the code for TEAR?   _____
14 If the code for RIGHT is <^/#> , what is /<^> ?   _____
15 If the code for BLAST is &*$^%, what is %$** ?   _____

TEST 12: **Mixed**

Test time: 0 — 5 — 10 minutes

Find the letter which will end the first word and start the second word.

Example   peac (h) ome

1. bro (___) and
2. mic (___) nds
3. pur (___) isk
4. kin (___) row
5. for (___) ish

Underline the number that completes each sequence.

6. 40 is to 20 as 30 is to (20, 60, 15).
7. 19 is to 17 as 35 is to (33, 37, 36).
8. 5 is to 20 as 6 is to (10, 24, 18).
9. 111 is to 222 as 333 is to (555, 444, 33).
10. 11 is to 22 as 7 is to (14, 19, 77).

In each line, underline the word which has its letters in alphabetical order.

11. fever   doubt   most   roof
12. baby   pray   take   foot
13. bitten   know   farm   daisy
14. birth   whole   blast   adder
15. slab   raid   flop   dark

Total

Test 13: **Mixed**

Test time: 0 — 5 — 10 minutes

Find and underline the two words which need to change places for each sentence to make sense.

Example   She went to <u>letter</u> the <u>write</u>.

1 The little waves bobbed on the boat.
2 I am so sleepy that I feel really tired.
3 That woman is wearing not a coat.
4 There was a rumble of storm as the thunder broke.
5 Please help your meal with the dad.

Change one word so that the sentence makes sense. Underline the word you are taking out and write your new word on the line.

Example   I waited in line to buy a <u>book</u> to see the film.   _ticket_

6 Please close the window, as we need some fresh air in the room.   _____
7 As the road was icy and dangerous, Mum drove fast.   _____
8 The postman emptied the postbox and put the carrots in his sack.   _____
9 Hurry up or we will be early for the bus.   _____
10 In Spring, the days start to get shorter and warmer.   _____

Underline one word in the brackets which is the most opposite in meaning to the word in capitals.

Example   WIDE   (broad   vague   long   <u>narrow</u>   motorway)

11 COOL   (distant   frosty   icy   cold   warm)
12 DANGER   (safety   risk   peril   accident road)
13 CLIMB   (ascend   mountain descend   ladder   stairs)
14 EXTREME   (slight   great   serious   sports   maximum)
15 DEPART   (appear   go   depend   arrive   exceed)

Total

Test 14: Mixed

Remove one letter from the word in capitals to leave a new word. The meaning of the new word is given in the clue.

| Example | AUNT | an insect | _ant_ |

1. WITCH   accompanying   _____
2. STABLE   not fresh   _____
3. SOFTEN   many times   _____
4. HARMFUL   amount you can carry   _____
5. MOTHER   alternative   _____

Find the four-letter word hidden at the end of one word and the beginning of the next word. The order of the letters may not be changed.

Example   The children had bat<u>s and</u> balls.   _sand_

6. Please close the middle window.   _____
7. The baby monkey scampered up the tree.   _____
8. Kittens can be quite playful.   _____
9. A little after four o'clock, he left.   _____
10. Yuriko and Sarah are coming as well.   _____

If the code for TRACTOR is WPFZWBP, what are the codes for the following words?

11. CART   _____
12. ROAR   _____
13. TACT   _____

Using the same code, decode:

14. ZBFW   _____
15. WPBW   _____

TEST 15: **Mixed**

Test time: 0 — 5 — 10 minutes

Rearrange the muddled words in capital letters so that each sentence makes sense.

Example There are sixty SNODCES _seconds_ in a UTMINE _minute_.

1–3 I am GIVANS _____ my TCPOKE _____ money to buy a new CYLBCEI _____ .

4–5 Don't CHOUT _____ that dog; it may TIEB _____.

Read the school timetable, and then work out how many minutes each of the following activities takes.

Assembly   9:00
Maths   9:20
English   10:00
Reading   10:45
Break   11:00

6 Assembly ____ minutes   **7** Maths ____ minutes
8 English ____ minutes   **9** Reading ____ minutes

I have 50p more than my sister, who has 80p less than my brother. My brother has £5.50.

10 How much does my sister have? _____

11 How much do I have? _____

Underline two words, one from each group, that go together to form a new word. The word in the first group always comes first.

Example (hand, <u>green</u>, for)   (light, <u>house</u>, sure)

12 (inter, ball, post)   (erupt, track, net)

13 (rain, suit, put)   (able, box, thing)

14 (sail, wasp, climb)   (or, up, bee)

15 (hard, my, be)   (time, bed, hind)

16

Total

TEST 16: **Mixed**

Test time: 0 — 5 — 10 minutes

Underline the two words, one from each group, which are the most opposite in meaning.

Example (dawn, <u>early</u>, wake) (<u>late</u>, stop, sunrise)

1 (still, cold, wet) (chilly, quiet, dry)
2 (hard, cap, pillow) (soft, hat, bed)
3 (change, shiny, coin) (money, dull, safe)
4 (circle, add, multiply) (line, number, divide)
5 (save, find, hide) (conceal, place, protect)

Look at these groups of words.
Group A: MALE   Group B: FEMALE
Choose the correct group for each of the following words. Write in the letter.

6 girl _____
7 bull _____
8 uncle _____
9 vixen _____
10 father _____

Give the missing groups of letters and numbers in the following sequences. The alphabet has been written out to help you.

A B C D E F G H I J K L M N O P Q R S T U V W X Y Z

Example	CQ	DP	EQ	FP	GQ	<u>HP</u>
11	ZY	XW	VU	TS	____	PO
12	____	bN	cM	dL	eK	fJ
13	4H	7G	4F	7E	4D	____
14	2X	4W	____	8U	10T	12S
15	QR	____	QT	QU	QV	QW

17

Time for a break! Go to Puzzle Page 42

Total

Test 17: Mixed

If a = 2, b = 5, c = 10, d = 4 and e = 3, find the value of the following calculations. Write the answer as a letter.

1. 2a + 2e = _____
2. de – c = _____
3. bc – cd = _____
4. 5b – 2c = _____
5. (b + d + e) – c = _____

Fill in the crosswords so that all the given words are included. You have been given one letter as a clue in each crossword.

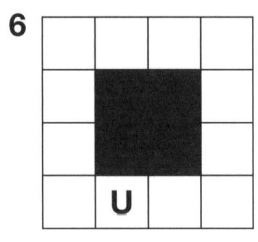

6. PARK KING
   PEEL LUNG

7. SMUG ATOM
   TART TANG

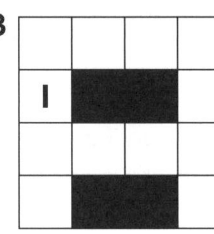

8. STEP NICE
   PINK PASS

9. FISH THAT
   WINE NEXT

Complete the following sentences by selecting the most sensible word from each group of words given in the brackets. Underline the words selected.

Example The (<u>children</u>, books, foxes) carried the (houses, <u>books</u>, steps) home from the (greengrocer, <u>library</u>, factory).

10. The (green, tiny, clean) (mouse, house, stone) scampered through the (happy, tall, metal) grass.

11. Dragons are said to have (short, scaly, slow) skin, a long (list, tail, step) and to (breathe, eat, climb) fire.

12. Neeta put (in, away, up) her (penguins, books, rocks) and went (on, out, by) for break.

13. If we (eat, walk, beat) over the common, we will get to the (swings, pencil, picture) where we can (play, fight, snow).

14. For (lunch, bucket, lessons) we had (seaside, sausages, paper), chips and (traffic, salad, rulers).

15. The (imaginary, happy, tattered) (book, scarecrow, postcard) frightened the birds away from the (library, fridge, field).

TEST 18: **Mixed**

Test time: 0 — 5 — 10 minutes

Fill in the missing numbers and letters in the following sequences.

Example	2	4	6	8	10	_12_
1	15	18	___	24	27	30
2	5	10	20	40	___	160
3	6.5	7.0	7.5	8.0	___	9.0
4	1J1	2K2	3L3	___	5N5	6O6
5	5	6	8	11	15	___

Add one letter to the word given in capital letters to make a new word. The meaning of the new word is given in the clue.

Example	PLAN	simple	_plain_
6	ALL	tumble	___
7	PICK	stab with a pin	___
8	OUR	tip out	___
9	STEAM	a little river	___
10	PAY	worship	___

If these words were placed in alphabetical order, which word would come last? Underline the word.

11	planet	space	rocket	moon	world
12	rabbit	horse	cat	dog	gerbil
13	traffic	tunnels	timber	thunder	tonsils
14	Friday	France	French	Frank	Freida
15	classical	claret	clarity	clarify	clarinet

TEST 19: Mixed

Rearrange the muddled words in capital letters so that each sentence makes sense.

Example There are sixty SNODCES _seconds_ in a UTMINE _minute_.

1–2 It is time to put on your STOAC _____ and go DEOTUIS _____ to play.

3–5 To reach the shops, you must turn GITRH _____ and walk ASTIRTHG _____ down the ETREST _____ to the end.

Complete the following sentences in the best way by choosing one word from each set of brackets.

Example Tall is to (tree, <u>short</u>, colour) as narrow is to (thin, white, <u>wide</u>).

6 Quick is to (slow, fast, yellow) as high is to (hill, low, green).

7 Pick is to (fruit, shovel, choose) as climb is to (descend, rise, steep).

8 Smooth is to (soft, skin, rough) as calm is to (boat, sunny, stormy).

9 Monday is to (yesterday, Tuesday, March) as Saturday is to (weekend, holiday, Sunday).

10 Paw is to (dog, toe, claw) as hoof is to (horse, shoe, kick).

These words have been written in code but the codes are not under the correct words. Find the correct code for each word.

STOP	POST	PORT	TRIP
7931	1657	5761	1697

11 STOP _____
12 POST _____
13 PORT _____
14 TRIP _____

Using the same code, decode:

15 51697 _____

TEST 20: **Mixed**

Test time: 0 — 5 — 10 minutes

Underline one word in the brackets which is the most opposite in meaning to the word in capitals.

Example	WIDE	(broad	vague	long	<u>narrow</u>	motorway)
1	DISPLAY	(hide	show	present	wall	picture)
2	MERRY	(joyful	Christmas	gloomy	jolly	full)
3	PRESENT	(gift	wrap	here	absent	leave)
4	SECURE	(sound	safe	locked	guard	unsafe)
5	STRIPED	(patterned	plain	marked	pyjamas	tie)

Find the three-letter word which can be added to the letters in capitals to make a new word. The new word will complete the sentence sensibly.

Example   The cat sprang onto the MO.   __USE__

6   The wind blew the SUNFLRS over in her garden.   _____

7   Take your muddy boots off before you tread on the CAR.   _____

8   After school, our CHER marks our books.   _____

9   The fairy godmother waved her magic W.   _____

10 His THBRUSH and toothpaste are on the shelf.   _____

Choose the word or phrase that makes each sentence true.

Example   A LIBRARY always has (posters, carpets, <u>books</u>, DVDs, stairs).

11 A DOG always has a (dinner, collar, nose, bone, lead).

12 A ROOM always has (a carpet, furniture, pictures, walls, a fire).

13 A WOOD always has (trees, leaves, squirrels, paths, grass).

14 A BOTTLE always has (glass, milk, wine, sides, a straw).

15 A SHOE always has (a sole, laces, polish, an owner, a sock).

TEST 21: **Mixed**

Test time: 0 — 5 — 10 minutes

Change the first word of the third pair in the same way as the other pairs to give a new word.

Example	bind, hind	bare, hare	but, __hut__
1	time, tame	wish, wash	stiff, _____
2	flame, fame	crane, cane	plain, _____
3	plug, gulp	doom, mood	dial, _____
4	bite, white	binge, whinge	bat, _____
5	meal, male	veal, vale	steal, _____

Underline the two words which are the odd ones out in the following groups of words.

Example	black	<u>king</u>	purple	green	<u>house</u>
6	foal	calf	beetle	duckling	wasp
7	many	some	lots	numerous	few
8	sum	add	metre	subtract	divide
9	line	talk	chat	row	discuss
10	anger	happy	rage	fury	laugh

Give the missing groups of letters and numbers in the following sequences. The alphabet has been written out to help you.

A B C D E F G H I J K L M N O P Q R S T U V W X Y Z

Example	CQ	DP	EQ	FP	GQ	__HP__
11	NM	LK	JI	_____	FE	DC
12	OPA	QRA	STA	UVA	WXA	_____
13	ab12	cd23	_____	gh45	ij56	kl67
14	9OP	8QR	9ST	8UV	_____	8YZ
15	ABB	_____	ADD	AEE	AFF	AGG

22

Total

TEST 22: **Mixed**

Test time: 0 5 10 minutes

Find a word that can be put in front of each of the following words to make new, compound words.

Example	cast	fall	ward	pour	_down_
1	writing	cuff	some	shake	_____
2	surfing	swept	mill	screen	_____
3	sheet	shop	man	out	_____
4	scotch	fly	fingers	cup	_____
5	land	light	way	brow	_____

From the information below, work out which flavours of chocolates are in each of the spaces in the chocolate box.

TOP

NOUGAT	A	B
C	TOFFEE	D
E	F	COFFEE CUP

BOTTOM

The Nut Cluster is next to the Strawberry Delight but directly below the Chocolate Almond.

The Chocolate Log is closer to the top than the Nut Cluster but directly below the Tangerine Surprise, which is next to the Caramel Melt.

6 Nut Cluster _____   7 Strawberry Delight _____
8 Chocolate Almond _____   9 Chocolate Log _____
10 Tangerine Surprise _____   11 Caramel Melt _____

Fill in the crosswords so that all the given words are included. You have been given one letter as a clue in each crossword.

12
ONLY GOOD
GAME MALE

13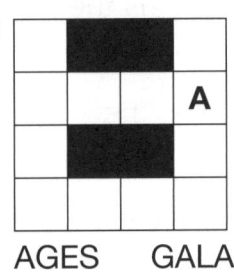
AGES GALA
SAFE HAZE

14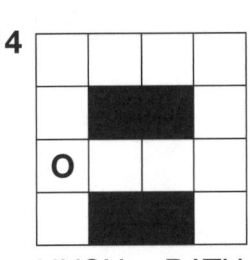
HUSH BATH
OWLS BOOK

15
JUMP TURN
ZULU SNIP

TEST 23: **Mixed**

Test time: 0 — 5 — 10 minutes

Find and underline the two words which need to change places for each sentence to make sense.

Example She went to <u>letter</u> the <u>write</u>.

1. Come in quietly as the baby is asleep fast.
2. The pub sign swung as it creaked in the wind.
3. I have right my books in the room on the left.
4. We are buying our car and selling a new one.
5. Please put the rail back on the towel.

Change one word so that the sentence makes sense. Underline the word you are taking out and write your new word on the line.

Example I waited in line to buy a <u>book</u> to see the film. _ticket_

6. As it is raining, we will stay outside and keep dry. _____
7. Fish are able to breathe out of water. _____
8. Tears poured from her ears as she was so unhappy. _____
9. The dog mooed happily when she saw her calf. _____
10. Lara fell up and cut her knee. _____

Solve each question by working out the code.

11. If the code for CHOIR is ~ # £ @ *, what is the code for RICH? _____
12. If the code for BASIN is GHYWC, what is the code for BINS? _____
13. If the code for TIGHT is 57935, what is the code for HIGH? _____
14. If the code for TRAIN is c b s l d, what is b s d c ? _____
15. If the code for FLOWN is − = + × > what is × + + = ? _____

Test 1: Similars and Opposites (page 2)

1 **story, tale** Both words mean an account of something, a yarn or narrative.
2 **sight, vision** Both words mean the ability to see.
3 **free, release** Both words mean to let go or liberate.
4 **dish, bowl** Both words mean a curved container to eat out of.
5 **finish, halt** Both words mean to stop.
6 **sensible, foolish** 'Sensible' means clear-headed or practical whereas 'foolish' means silly or unwise.
7 **war, peace** 'War' means fighting or conflict whereas 'peace' is calm or harmony.
8 **heavy, light** 'Heavy' means weighty whereas 'light' means weightless.
9 **rise, fall** 'Rise' is when something goes up whereas 'fall' is when something goes down.
10 **major, minor** 'Major' is something large or important whereas 'minor' is smaller or less important.
11 **fib** 'Lie' and 'fib' both mean something that is not true.
12 **capture** 'Catch' and 'capture' mean to seize or imprison.
13 **lady** 'Woman' and 'lady' are both grown-up females.
14 **blend** 'Combine' and 'blend' both mean to mix.
15 **attack** 'Charge' and 'attack' both mean to rush in and fight.

Test 2: Sorting Words (page 3)

1 **FIREWORK**   2 **SUNDAY**
3 **MOWING**   4 **QUIET**
5 **PICTURE**

6–10 Group A contains the counties of Kent and Durham. Group B contains the planets of Saturn, Venus and Mars.
  6 **A**   7 **B**
  8 **B**   9 **A**
  10 **B**
11 **simple, easy** The other words all mean tricky or complicated.
12 **horse, wood** The other words are all footwear.
13 **clock, sea** The other words all mean to study or examine.
14 **brown, black** The other words are all shades of red.
15 **tiny, little** The other words all mean massive or vast.

Test 3: Selecting Letters (page 4)

1 **e** vale, each   2 **b** lamb, book
3 **f** half, fish   4 **z** jazz, zone
5 **e** care, echo   6 bus**t**
7 lo**n**g   8 **f**rail
9 p**a**int   10 fl**o**at
11 **w**in   12 **h**eat
13 **c**ane   14 **b**each
15 **l**ight

Test 4: Selecting Words (page 5)

1 **forehead**   2 **chatterbox**
3 **highlight**   4 **mushroom**
5 **upset**

6–10 Try each of the words in the first set of brackets. Do they make sense with any words in the second and third brackets? Only one combination of three words makes sense.
  6 **night, bed, teeth**
  7 **coat, blue, red**
  8 **hungry, dog, bone**
  9 **rusty, gate, squeaked**
  10 **rained, deep, playground**
11 **water** A lake must have water to be a lake. It may have the others things.
12 **grass** A lawn is made up of grass that has been mown.
13 **face** All animals have faces. A dog may also have the other things.
14 **tarmac** A main road is a large road that has a smooth surface of tarmac on it.
15 **sides** A dustbin is a solid shape and shapes have sides.

Test 5: Finding Words (page 6)

1 **ALL** balloon   2 **RAN** orange
3 **TEA** team   4 **DEN** garden
5 **WIN** swings
6 **seat** Plea**se at**tach the labels to your jackets.
7 **them** **The m**atch is hanging in the balance.
8 **wear** It is a good thing **we ar**e firm friends.
9 **term** My sis**ter m**akes me tidy my room.
10 **germ** Cutting my fin**ger m**ade me cry.
11 **snail** There is no 'i' in 'candles'.
12 **state** There is only one 't' in 'baskets'.
13 **thief** There is no 'i' in 'feather'.
14 **crawl** There is no 'w' in 'clamber'.
15 **trees** There is no 's' in 'treacle'.

EXPANDED ANSWERS

Bond VR 10 Minute Tests 8–9 years

Test 6: Alphabetical Order and Substitution (page 7)

1 brown
2 chest
3 August
4 abbot
5 bossy
6 ghost
7 glory
8 added
9 faced
10 bead
11 **20** 8 + 9 + 3 = 20
12 **10** (2 × 2) + (2 × 3) = 10
13 **19** (3 × 9) − 8 = 19
14 **4** (9 − 8) + 3 = 4
15 **22** 8 + 2 + 9 + 3 = 22

Test 7: Word Progressions (page 8)

1–5 Use grids as shown below to help work out the missing word.

1 STIR

		1	2		3	4	
	B	U	S	H	O	P	E	N

		1	2		3	4	
	R	U	S	T	I	R	O	N

2 PASS

1	2				3	4
C	A	R	S	R	I	P	E

1	2				3	4
P	A	R	K	L	E	S	S

3 MORE

1	2			3	4	
H	O	R	N	L	E	A	P

1	2			3	4	
M	O	O	N	R	E	A	L

4 FIRE

1				2	3	4
C	H	I	P	W	A	K	E

1				2	3	4
F	L	A	N	H	I	R	E

5 TIRE
6 CASE
7 FIRM
8 **cure** The pattern is change the second letter of the first word from 'a' to 'u'.
9 **gong** The pattern is to change the first letter from 's' to 'g'.
10 **hit** The pattern is to remove the last two letters of the first word, leaving a three-letter word.
11 **sewn** The pattern is to swap over the first and last letters of the first word.
12–15 Solve these questions by looking at the first set of three and working out how the first and last numbers have been used to arrive at the middle number. Apply this to the second set of three and see if it works. If it does, apply it to the last set.
12 **9** 3 + 1 = 4 and 5 + 2 = 7, so 8 + 1 = 9
13 **3** 6 − 1 = 5 and 4 − 1 = 3, so 8 − 5 = 3
14 **10** 8 + 3 = 11 and 7 + 5 = 12, so 6 + 4 = 10
15 **9** 2 × 3 = 6 and 4 × 2 = 8, so 3 × 3 = 9

Test 8: Logic (page 9)

1–3 A table is the easiest way to sort the information, like this:

CHILDREN	TROUSERS	TOPS
Amy	jeans	blue
Tom	jeans	green
Raj	tracksuit bottoms	green
Billie	tracksuit bottoms	blue

1 **Billie**
2 **No**
3 **Jeans**
4 **10:25** 15 + 10 = 25, so 10:25
5 **10:50** 25 + 5 + 20 = 50, so 10:50
6–8 Use a diagram to help you:

2	4	6	8	10	12	14	16	18	20
-	-	S	T	R	E	E	T	-	-
1	3	5	7	9	11	13	15	17	19

6 **6**
7 **15**
8 **12**
9–10 A table is the easiest way to sort the information, like this:

	Football boots	Cricket boots	Running shoes	Tennis shoes
Jake	✓	✓		
Holly	✓		✓	
Sana		✓		✓
Stuart			✓	✓

9 **Sana**
10 **Holly**
11 **1 hour 30 minutes** If it takes 45 minutes to cook 1 kg of meat, then twice that is 90 minutes or 1 hour and 30 minutes.
12 **11:30** The joint takes 1 hour and 30 minutes so needs to be in the oven at 11:30.
13 **11:50** The potatoes take 70 minutes (= 1 hour and 10 minutes), so need to be in the oven at 11:50.

14–15 Use a table to help you:

Wednesday	Day before yesterday
Thursday	Yesterday
Friday	Today
Saturday	Tomorrow
Sunday	Day after tomorrow

14 Friday
15 Sunday

Test 9: Codes (page 10)

1 **ZKMH** B = Z, E = K, A = M, R = H
2 **HMP** R = H, A = M, W = P
3 **ZHKP** B = Z, R = H, E = K, W = P
4 **BARE** Z = B, M = A, H = R, K = E
5 **WEAR** P = W, K = E, M = A, H = R
6–10 One of the number codes has a repeated number in the middle so 1993 = NEED. Knowing E = 9 and N = 1, then CANE = 7619 and, therefore, HAND = 4613 because they both have N (1) as the third letter. 9674 = EACH as E = 1 and A = 6 (as in CANE and HAND). So the missing code for ACHE = 6749.
6 **4613**
7 **9674**
8 **7619**
9 **6749**
10 **1993**
11 **2169** D = 2, A = 1, T = 6, E = 9
12 **FOVD** B = F, A = O, T = V, S = D
13 **YPRX** M = Y, I = P, L = R, E = X
14 **PINT** 3 = P, 9 = I, 6 = N, 8 = T
15 **MEET** * = M, = = E, = = E, $ = T.

Test 10: Sequences (page 11)

1 **slow, clean** 'Quick' and 'slow' are opposites in the same way 'dirty' and 'clean' are opposites.
2 **head, hand** A 'hat' is worn on a 'head' in the same way a 'glove' is worn on a 'hand'.
3 **six, ten** 'Three' is half of 'six' in the same way 'five' is half of 'ten'.
4 **throw, fall** 'Catch' and 'throw' are opposites in the same way 'rise' is opposite of 'fall'.
5 **depart, little** 'Go' and 'depart' are similar in the same way 'small' is similar to 'little'.
6 **DB** Each letter in the first pair moves backwards by four places in the second pair.
7 **10d** The numbers decrease by 2. The letters move forwards by one place.
8 **MNP** Each letter in the first grouping moves forwards by four places in the second grouping.
9 **Q4R** The letters move forward by two places. The numbers increase by 1.

10 **NO** This pattern is the ordinary alphabetical order.
11 **FV** The first letter is a repeating pattern: FFFGGG. The second letter moves backwards one alphabetical place.
12 **AC** Both letters move forwards by four places in the alphabet.
13 **19** The numbers increase by 4 each time.
14 **12** The numbers decrease by 3 each time.
15 **2** The number doubles each time.

Test 11: Mixed (page 12)

1 **DENTIST**
2 **FOOTBALL**
3 **SUMMER**
4 **PLAYING**
5 **PELICAN**
6 **salty, sweet** 'Salty' and 'sweet' are opposites in taste or flavour.
7 **flexible, rigid** 'Flexible' means bendable whereas 'rigid' is unbendable.
8 **fail, pass** 'Fail' means to not succeed whereas 'pass' means to attain the appropriate standard.
9 **sensible, foolish** 'Sensible' means wise whereas 'foolish' means silly.
10 **to, from** 'To' means going towards something whereas 'from' means going away from something.
11 **PDRL** S = P, H = D, O = R, E = L
12 **3270** M = 3, E = 2, S = 7, H = 0
13 **VMCF** T = V, E = M, A = C, R = F
14 **GRIT** / = G, < = R, ^ = I, > = T
15 **TALL** % = T, $ = A, * = L, * = L

Test 12: Mixed (page 13)

1 **w** brow, wand
2 **e** mice, ends
3 **r** purr, risk
4 **g** king, grow
5 **d** ford, dish
6 **15** The second number is half of the first number so half of 30 is 15.
7 **33** The first number decreases by 2 so 35 − 2 = 33.
8 **24** The first number is multiplied by 4 to make the second number so 6 × 4 = 24.
9 **444** The first number increases by 111, so 333 + 111 = 444.
10 **14** The first number is doubled to make the second number so 7 × 2 = 14.
11 **most**
12 **foot**
13 **know**
14 **adder**
15 **flop**

Test 13: Mixed (page 14)

1. The little **boat** bobbed on the **waves**.
2. I am so **tired** that I feel really **sleepy**.
3. That woman is **not wearing** a coat.
4. There was a rumble of **thunder** as the **storm** broke.
5. Please help your **dad** with the **meal**.
6. **close, open** Please open the window, as we need some fresh air in the room.
7. **fast, slowly** As the road was icy and dangerous, Mum drove slowly.
8. **carrots, letters** The postman emptied the postbox and put the letters in his sack.
9. **early, late** Hurry up or we will be late for the bus.
10. **shorter, longer** In Spring, the days start to get longer and warmer.
11. **warm** 'Cool' and 'warm' are opposites as 'cool' is on the way to being cold and warm is on the way to being hot.
12. **safety** 'Danger' means peril whereas 'safety' is security.
13. **descend** To 'climb' is to go up whereas to 'descend' is to go down.
14. **slight** 'Slight' is a little bit whereas 'extreme' is at great length.
15. **arrive** 'Depart' is to go whereas 'arrive' is to come.

Test 14: Mixed (page 15)

1. with
2. stale
3. often
4. armful
5. other
6. **them** Please close **the m**iddle window.
7. **keys** The baby mon**key s**campered up the tree.
8. **scan** Kitten**s can** be quite playful.
9. **leaf** A litt**le af**ter four o'clock, he left.
10. **hare** Yuriko and Sar**ah are** coming as well.
11. **ZFPW** C = Z, A = F, R = P, T = W
12. **PBFP** R = P, O = B, A = F, R = P
13. **WFZW** T = W, A = F, C = Z, T = W
14. **COAT** Z = C, B = O, F = A, W = T
15. **TROT** W = T, P = R, B = O, W = T

Test 15: Mixed (page 16)

1–3 saving, pocket, bicycle
4–5 touch, bite
6. **20** From 9:00 to 9:20 is twenty minutes.
7. **40** From 9:20 to 10:00 is forty minutes.
8. **45** 10:00 to 10:45 is forty-five minutes.
9. **15** 10:45 to 11:00 is fifteen minutes.
10. **£4.70** If my sister has 80p less than my brother who has £5.50, she has £4.70.
11. **£5.20** If I have 50p more than my sister who has £4.70, then I have £5.20.
12. internet
13. suitable
14. sailor
15. behind

Test 16: Mixed (page 17)

1. **wet, dry** 'Wet' and 'dry' are the most opposite as 'wet' means sodden whereas 'dry' means waterless.
2. **hard, soft** 'Hard' and 'soft' are the most opposite as 'hard' means tough and unbending whereas 'soft' means squishy and gentle.
3. **shiny, dull** 'Shiny' and 'dull' are the most opposite as 'shiny' means bright whereas 'dull' means dreary.
4. **multiply, divide** 'Multiply' and 'divide' are the most opposite as 'multiply' means to increase whereas 'divide' is to make less.
5. **find, conceal** 'Find' and 'conceal' are the most opposite as 'find' is to discover something whereas 'conceal' is to hide it.
6. B
7. A
8. A
9. B
10. A
11. **RQ** In this sequence, the alphabet has been written backwards.
12. **aO** The first letter in each pair moves forward one place. The second letter in each pair moves backwards one place.
13. **7C** The numbers in each pair are in a repeating pattern: 474747. The letters move backwards by one letter.
14. **6V** The numbers in each pair increase by 2. The letters in each pair move backwards one place.
15. **QS** The first letter in each pair is in a repeating pattern: QQQQQQ. The second letter in each pair move forwards one place.

Test 17: Mixed (page 18)

1. **c** $(2 \times 2) + (2 \times 3) = 10$ $10 = c$
2. **a** $(4 \times 3) - 10 = 2$ $2 = a$
3. **c** $(5 \times 10) - (10 \times 4) = 10$ $10 = c$
4. **b** $(5 \times 5) - (2 \times 10) = 5$ $5 = b$
5. **a** $(5 + 4 + 3) - 10 = 2$ $2 = a$

6.

7.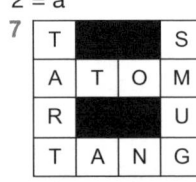

8.

9.

10–15 Try each of the words in the first set of brackets. Do they make sense with any words in the second and third brackets? Only one combination of three words makes sense.
10 **tiny, mouse, tall**
11 **scaly, tail, breathe**
12 **away, books, out**
13 **walk, swings, play**
14 **lunch, sausages, salad**
15 **tattered, scarecrow, field**

Test 18: Mixed (page 19)

1 **21** The numbers increase by 3 each time.
2 **80** The numbers double each time, so 2 × 40 = 80
3 **8.5** The numbers increase by 0.5 each time.
4 **4M4** Both numbers increase by 1. The letters move forwards one alphabetical place so 3L3 becomes 4M4.
5 **20** The number added increases by 1 each time: +1, +2, +3, +4, +5, so 15 + 5 = 20
6 **fall**   7 **prick**   8 **pour**
9 **stream**   10 **pray**   11 **world**
12 **rabbit**
13–16 Where you need to look beyond the first letter to work out the alphabetical order, use tables to help you:
13 **tunnels**

t	r	a	f	f	i	c
t	u	n	n	e	l	s
t	i	m	b	e	r	
t	h	u	n	d	e	r
t	o	n	s	i	l	s

14 **Friday**

F	r	i	d	a	y
F	r	a	n	c	e
F	r	e	n	c	h
F	r	a	n	k	
F	r	e	i	d	a

15 **classical**

c	l	a	s	s	i	c	a	l
c	l	a	r	e	t			
c	l	a	r	i	t	y		
c	l	a	r	i	f	y		
c	l	a	r	i	n	e	t	

Test 19: Mixed (page 20)

1–2 **coats, outside**
3–5 **right, straight, street**
6 **slow, low** 'Quick' and 'slow' are opposites in the same way as 'high' and 'low' are opposites.
7 **choose, rise** 'Pick' and 'choose' both mean select in the same way as 'ascend' and 'rise' both mean to go upwards.
8 **rough, stormy** 'Smooth' and 'rough' are opposites in the same way as 'calm' and 'stormy' are opposites.
9 **Tuesday, Sunday** 'Tuesday' is the day after 'Monday'; in the same way, 'Sunday' is the day after 'Saturday'.
10 **dog, horse** A 'dog' has a 'paw' in the same way as a 'horse' has a 'hoof'.
11–15 Two of the words begin with 'PO', so P = 1 and O = 6, and T = 7 because both words end with 'T'. Therefore, 'TRIP' = 7931. From this, you can deduce all the letters.
11 **5761** S = 5, T = 7, O = 6, P = 1
12 **1657** P = 1, O = 6, S = 5, T = 7
13 **1697** P = 1, O = 6, R = 9, T = 7
14 **7931** T = 7, R = 9, I = 3, P = 1
15 **SPORT** S = 5, P = 1, O = 6, R = 9, T = 7, so SPORT = 51697.

Test 20: Mixed (page 21)

1 **hide** 'Display' means to show whereas 'hide' means to conceal.
2 **gloomy** 'Merry' means cheerful whereas 'gloomy' means miserable.
3 **absent** 'Present' means to be here whereas 'absent' means missing or not here.
4 **unsafe** 'Secure' means safe whereas 'unsafe' means dangerous or insecure.
5 **plain** 'Striped' means patterned whereas 'plain' is one colour or design.
6 **OWE** sunflowers   7 **PET** carpet
8 **TEA** teacher   9 **AND** wand
10 **TOO** toothbrush
11 **nose** A dog may possess the other items but a 'nose' is part of its body.
12 **walls** A room may be furnished with the other items but 'walls' are part of its structure.
13 **trees** Other things may be in a wood but a wood must have 'trees' to be a wood.
14 **sides** A bottle is a solid shape so it must have sides. It could be made of glass but may not.
15 **a sole** A shoe could have the other things but it must have a sole to protect the foot.

Test 21: Mixed (page 22)

1 **staff** The pattern is to change the second letter from 'i' to 'a'.
2 **pain** The pattern is to remove the second letter.
3 **laid** The pattern is to reverse the order of the letters.

4 **what** The pattern is to remove 'b' from the beginning of the word and replace it with 'wh'.
5 **stale** The pattern is to move the letter 'e' to the end of the word.
6 **beetle, wasp** The other words are all baby animals.
7 **some, few** The other words indicate plenty of something.
8 **sum, metre** The other words are verbs for mathematical calculations.
9 **line, row** The other words are all means of talking or communicating in a calm way. ('Row' can mean to argue.)
10 **happy, laugh** The other words are nouns indicating annoyance or wrath.
11 **HG** The pattern here is a section of the alphabet in reverse order.
12 **YZA** The first and second letters are in alphabetical order: OP QR ST UV WX YZ. The third letter is a repeated pattern: AAAAAA.
13 **ef34** The letters are in alphabetical order: ab cd ef gh ij kl. The numbers increase by 11 each time.
14 **9WX** The numbers are a repeated pattern: 989898. The letters are in alphabetical order: OP QR ST UV WX YZ.
15 **ACC** The first letter is a repeated pattern: AAAAAA. The second and third letters are in alphabetical order, repeated: BB, CC, DD, EE, FF, GG.

Test 22: Mixed (page 23)

1 **hand** handwriting, handcuff, handsome, handshake
2 **wind** windsurfing, windswept, windmill, windscreen
3 **work** worksheet, workshop, workman, workout
4 **butter** butterscotch, butterfly, butterfingers, buttercup
5 **high** highland, highlight, highway, highbrow
6–11 As the Nut Cluster is next to the Strawberry Delight and under the Chocolate Almond, the Nut Cluster must be E, Strawberry Delight must be F and the Chocolate Almond is C. If the Chocolate Log is directly below the Tangerine Surprise, it must be D with the Tangerine Surprise in B, leaving the Caramel Melt as A.
6 **E** 7 **F** 8 **C**
9 **D** 10 **B** 11 **A**
12 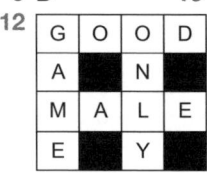 13

14  15

Test 23: Mixed (page 24)

1 Come in quietly as the baby is **fast** **asleep**.
2 The pub sign **creaked** as it **swung** in the wind.
3 I have **left** my books in the room on the **right**.
4 We are **selling** our car and **buying** a new one.
5 Please put the **towel** back on the **rail**.
6 **outside, inside** As it is raining, we will stay inside and keep dry.
7 **able, unable** Fish are unable to breathe out of water.
8 **ears, eyes** Tears poured from her eyes as she was so unhappy.
9 **dog, cow** The cow mooed happily when she saw her calf.
10 **up, down** Lara fell down and cut her knee.
11 * @ ~ # R = *, I = @, C = ~, H = #
12 **GWCY** B = G, I = W, N = C, S = Y
13 **3793** H = 3, I = 7, G = 9, H = 3
14 **RANT** b = R, s = A, d = N, c = T
15 **WOOL** x = W, + = O, + = O, = = L

Test 24: Mixed (page 25)

1 **lie, truth** A 'lie' is a fib whereas 'truth' is a certainty.
2 **backwards, forwards** 'Backwards' is reversing whereas 'forwards' is moving onwards.
3 **dawn, dusk** 'Dawn' is the beginning of the day when the sun is rising whereas 'dusk' is when the sun is setting at the end of the day.
4 **broad, narrow** 'Broad' is wide whereas 'narrow' is thin.
5 **far, near** 'Far' is a long way away whereas 'near' is close by.
6 **8** (3 + 10) − 5 = 8   7 **12** 6 × 2 = 12
8 **20** 2 + 3 + 5 + 10 = 20   9 **t** 5 × 2 = 10   10 = t
10 **t** 2 + 3 + 5 = 10   10 = t   11 **chief**
12 **labelled**   13 **decide**
14 **dabble**   15 **jackal**

Test 25: Mixed (page 26)

1 **LAP, PAL**   2 **DRAW, WARD**
3 **APT, TAP**   4 **LEFT, FELT**
5 **BEARD, BREAD**
6–10 Use grids as shown below to help work out the missing word.

6 BEAR

1	2			3	4	
D	E	N	T	S	K	I	P

1	2			3	4	
B	E	A	N	A	R	C	H

7 POOR

1			4	2/3*	2/3*	
F	E	L	T	B	O	O	K

1			4	2/3*	2/3*	
P	E	A	R	S	O	O	T

8 PIES

1	2				3	4
L	I	F	E	T	A	P	S

1	2				3	4
P	I	L	E	E	Y	E	S

9 WIDE

1	2			3	4	
G	I	F	T	V	E	S	T

1	2			3	4	
W	I	S	H	D	E	F	Y

10 HAZY

1				2/3*	2/3*	4
M	I	L	K	S	O	O	N

1				2/3*	2/3*	4
H	I	G	H	L	A	Z	Y

11 **outside, under** 'Inside' and 'outside' are opposites in the same way as 'over' and 'under' are opposites.
12 **large, little** 'Big' is similar to 'large' in the same way as 'small' is similar to 'little'.
13 **head, finger** 'Hair' is found on a 'head' as a 'nail' is found on a 'finger'.
14 **pen, brush** 'Ink' makes the marks from a 'pen' in the same way as 'paint' makes the marks from a 'brush'.
15 **firm, smooth** 'Slippery' is the opposite of 'firm' in the same way as 'bumpy' is the opposite of 'smooth'.

Test 26: Mixed (page 27)

1 **peculiar** 'Strange' and 'peculiar' both mean odd or unusual.
2 **annoy** 'Vex' and 'annoy' both mean to irritate or aggravate.
3 **direct** 'Straight' and 'direct' both mean taking the shortest route.
4 **glance** 'Peep' and 'glance' are both quick ways of looking at someone or something.
5 **pour** 'Tip' and 'pour' both mean to empty, usually liquid, out of something.
6 **four** Please take those coats o**f f our** chairs.
7 **wine** Ravi is so quick, he will **win e**very race.
8 **hate** Sara**h ate** a whole tin of toffees.
9 **nest** O**ne st**ar is shining particularly brightly.
10 **they** Leaves are blowing in the air in **the y**ard
11 **tank**   12 **angle**   13 **swam**
14 **sight**   15 **step**

Test 27: Mixed (page 28)

1 **MINE**   2 **SLOT**   3 **BASH**
4 **LUNG**   5 **BEAT**
6 **garden, letter** The other words all refer to the worth of something.
7 **oval, circle** The other words are shapes with straight sides.
8 **one, two** These are cardinal or ordinary numbers whereas the others ('third', 'fourth', 'fifth') are ordinal numbers used as adjectives.
9 **money, shop** The other words all mean the financial value of something.
10 **dark, tough** The other words all mean fragile or insubstantial.
11–15 Solve these questions by looking at the first set of three and working out how the first and last numbers have been used to arrive at the middle number. Apply this to the second set of three and see if it works. If it does, apply it to the last set.
11 **12** $16 - 2 = 14$ and $24 - 12 = 12$, so $18 - 6 = 12$
12 **1** $20 \div 4 = 5$ and $10 \div 5 = 2$, so $8 \div 8 = 1$
13 **11** $3 + 4 = 7$ and $5 + 8 = 13$, so $4 + 7 = 11$
14 **9** $5 \times 5 = 25$ and $4 \times 4 = 16$, so $3 \times 3 = 9$
15 **2** $8 \div 4 = 2$ and $12 \div 4 = 3$, so $12 \div 6 = 2$

Test 28: Mixed (page 29)

1 **VX** Both letters move forward three alphabetical places.
2 **13G** The numbers decrease by 2 (19, 17; 15, 13). The letters move forwards one alphabetical place.
3 **CB** Both letters move backwards two alphabetical places.
4 **G4H** Both letters move forwards two alphabetical places. The numbers increase by 1.
5 **wxy** Each group of three letters in alphabetical order is followed by the next three letters in the alphabet.
6 **f** farm, fattest, fox, fling
7 **b** brain, bright, blast, blank

8 **n** nape, nought, nail, nice
9 **e** eager, empty, eat, eyes
10 **c** climb, crust, crash, clock
11 **lift, raise** 'Lift' and 'raise' both mean to cause to go upwards.
12 **wander, stray** Both words mean to roam or ramble aimlessly.
13 **weird, odd** Both words mean bizarre or unusual.
14 **furry, hairy** Both words mean covered in hair or fur.
15 **fight, battle** Both words mean to strive or to struggle, often in combat.

Test 29: Mixed (page 30)

1–5 Two of the words begin with 'L' so L = Q and M = H. Therefore, MILK = HPQJ and FILM = CPQH. From this, you can work out all the letters and their codes.
1 **HPQJ** M = H, I = P, L = Q, K = J
2 **CPQH** F = C, I = P, L = Q, M = H
3 **QXHR** L = Q, A = X, M = H, B = R
4 **QPHZ** L = Q, I = P, M = H, P = Z
5 **BALL** R = B, X = A, Q = L, Q = L
6 **peel, skin** Both the words mean the outer covering.
7 **reply, respond** Both the words mean to answer.
8 **giggle, chuckle** Both the words mean to laugh.
9 **gather assemble** Both the words mean to group together.
10 **entire, complete** Both the words mean whole.
11 **boring** The pattern is to remove the last letter in the first word and replace it with 'ing'.
12 **bush** The pattern is to remove the 't' at the end of the first word and replace it with 'h'.
13 **wolf** The pattern is to reverse the letters of the first word.
14 **from** The pattern is to swap the second and third letters of the first word.
15 **star** The pattern is to remove the last two letters of the first word.

Test 30: Mixed (page 31)

1 **19** (3 × 8) − 5 = 19   2 **17** (2 × 5) + 7 = 17
3 **12** (3 × 7) − (3 × 3) = 12   4 **20** 8 + 5 + 7 = 20
5 **3** 8 − 5 = 3
6 **THE** there
7 **ARC** parcels
8 **HUT** shut
9 **ASH** splashed
10 **AIR** armchair
11 ten__t__
12 was__p__
13 f__i__rst
14 pl__a__in
15 st__ee__p

Test 31: Mixed (page 32)

1 **5493** M = 5, A = 4, K = 9, E = 3
2 **2745** T = 2, R = 7, A = 4, M = 5
3 **2453** T = 2, A = 4, M = 5, E = 3
4 **TEAM** 2 = T, 3 = E, 4 = A, 5 = M
5 **MATE** 5 = M, 4 = A, 2 = T, 3 = E
6 **legs** A beetle may have the other items but it must have legs to move.
7 **a mattress** A bed may have the other items but needs a mattress on its frame.
8 **pages** A book is made up of pages. It must have these to be a book.
9 **wheels** A car has to have wheels to be a form of transport.
10 **food** Groceries are things we eat so a grocery shop must have food.
11–15 Use grids as shown below to help work out the missing word.

11 **PILE**

1	2			3	4	
B	E	L	T	A	N	T	S

1	2			3	4	
P	I	C	K	L	E	A	N

12 **FLAP**

1	2				3	4
Q	U	I	P	B	R	A	Y

1	2				3	4
F	L	E	W	S	W	A	P

13 **WADE**

1				2	3	4
J	A	M	S	C	O	I	N

1				2	3	4
W	E	S	T	F	A	D	E

14 **FOOL**

1			4	2/3*	2/3*	
S	P	U	N	W	O	O	L

1			4	2/3*	2/3*	
F	A	I	L	T	O	O	K

15 **MICE**

1	2				3	4
K	I	N	G	S	A	L	T

1	2				3	4
M	I	L	K	F	A	C	E

Test 32: Mixed (page 33)

1. **h** path, hope
2. **t** belt, than
3. **o** hero, once
4. **w** claw, wise
5. **k** back, kite
6. **tour** All of us caugh**t our** balls.
7. **vest** The wa**ves t**ossed the boat.
8. **card** The old **car d**oor was very rusty.
9. **dove** The horse jumpe**d ove**r the fence.
10. **than** Bo**th an**imals were extremely fierce.
11. **grin** There is no 'r' in 'thinking'.
12. **blade** There is no 'd' in 'battles'.
13. **nose** There is no 'e' in 'cushion'.
14. **drain** There is no 'n' in 'birthday'.
15. **roast** There is no 'a' in 'history'.

Test 33: Mixed (page 34)

1. VEST / A_E / ICED / N_N
2. WASH / A_O / L_O / LINK
3. H_J / ALSO / R_L / MUST
4. SNUB / N_A / O_S / WITH

5–10 Use a grid to help you:

	ballet	dancing	tennis	scouts	football	art	music	athletics	swimming
Mon	A, C								D, E
Tues						C			
Wed			B, D						
Thur		A, E					C		
Fri									
Sat			A, E					C	
Sun					B, D				

5. **2**
6. **art**
7. **Friday**
8. **Child C**
9. **Child B**
10. **Child C**
11. **munch, chat** 'Chew' is similar to 'munch' in the same way as 'talk' is to 'chat'.
12. **month, day** 'February is a 'month' in the same way as 'Sunday' is a 'day' of the week.
13. **peace, happiness** 'War' is the opposite of 'peace' in the same way as 'sadness' is the opposite of 'happiness'.
14. **cushion, mat** A 'pillow' is similar to a 'cushion' in the same way a 'rug' is similar to a 'mat'.
15. **4 legs, 2 legs** A 'cat' has '4 legs' in the same way a 'man' has '2 legs'.

Test 34: Mixed (page 35)

1. **11** The numbers increase by 4 each time.
2. **75** The numbers increase by 11 each time.
3. **8** The numbers double each time.
4. **9** The number subtracted decreases by 1 each time: −5, −4, −3, −2, −1
5. **10y** The numbers increase by 3 each time. The letters move backwards one place each time.
6. **Leeds, London** The other words are all countries.
7. **left, dark** The other words all mean just or fair-minded.
8. **cloud, basin** The other words are all sources of light.
9. **mirror, picture** The other words are all things you can read.
10. **daughter, mother** The other words are all male.
11. **nervous** 'Timid' and 'nervous' both mean easily scared.
12. **chief** 'Main' and 'chief' both mean the leading or most important part.
13. **beneath** 'Under' and 'beneath' both mean below something.
14. **changeable** 'Variable' and 'changeable' both mean able to alter or shift.
15. **burn** 'Singe' and 'burn' both mean to char or damage with a flame.

Test 35: Mixed (page 36)

1. **APE, PEA**
2. **LAIR, RAIL**
3. **REAR, RARE**
4. **ITS, SIT**
5. **TASTE, STATE**

6.
7.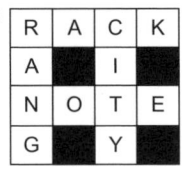
8.
9.

10–15 Try each of the words in the first set of brackets. Do they make sense with any words in the second and third brackets? Only one combination of three words makes sense.

10. **controlled, passed, goal**
11. **listen, instructions, shouted**
12. **that, iceberg, water**
13. **sheep, horns, not**
14. **finished, writing, play**
15. **school, learning, life**

Test 36: Mixed (page 37)

1. **OWN** down
2. **YES** eyes
3. **RAN** grandmother
4. **OUR** hour
5. **TEN** kittens
6. **cats** 12 + 9 = 21
7. **dogs** dogs = 7, fish = 6
8. **5** 2 + 3 = 5
9. **others** 11
10. **fish** Class Y have 6 fish, Class X has only 3 fish.
11. **20** 2 + 7 + 11 = 20
12. **bathroom**
13. **bitten**
14. **knowledge**
15. **quicksand**

Test 37: Mixed (page 38)

1.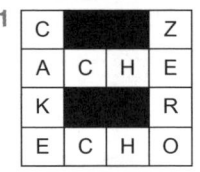
2.
3.
4.

5–8 Use a diagram to help you:

2	4	6	8	10	12	14	16	18	20
-	-	S	T	R	E	E	T	-	-
1	3	5	7	9	11	13	15	17	19

5. **8**
6. **13**
7. **19**
8. **9**

9–10 A table is the easiest way to sort the information, like this:

	Blue door	Window boxes	Door knockers	Green door
3	✓		✓	
4	✓	✓		
5		✓		✓
6			✓	✓

9. **6**
10. **4**
11. **B** A boat goes on water.
12. **A** A train goes on land.
13. **B** A ship goes on water.
14. **A** A van goes on land.
15. **C** A helicopter goes in the air.

Test 38: Mixed (page 39)

1. **h** heel, hearth, heat, hand
2. **p** pram, please, pink, pitch
3. **d** devil, dear, dark, drink
4. **s** sport, sweep, steam, stray
5. **k** knit, kill, knot, knight
6. **breadth, width** Both words are to do with the size of an object.
7. **save, conserve** Both words mean to keep safe or preserve.
8. **tint, hue** Both words mean a colour.
9. **knot, fasten** Both words mean to tie or secure.
10. **smooth, silky** Both words mean shiny or flat – the opposite of rough.

11–15 Arrange the words in a grid to make it easier to put them in the correct alphabetical order.

11. **talk**

t	a	l	k			4
c	o	n	v	e	r	s	e	2
s	h	o	u	t		3
y	e	l	l			5
c	a	l	l			1

12. **low**

h	i	g	h		3
l	o	w			4
b	e	l	o	w	2
a	b	o	v	e	1
u	p				5

13. **sandwich**

b	i	s	c	u	i	t	1
c	a	k	e				2
s	a	n	d	w	i	c	h	4
c	o	o	k	i	e		3
t	a	r	t				5

14. **screw**

s	c	r	e	w		4
n	a	i	l			2
t	a	c	k			5
p	i	n				3
h	a	m	m	e	r	1

15. **night**

l	i	g	h	t		3
d	a	r	k			1
n	i	g	h	t		4
d	a	y				2
s	u	n	s	h	i	n	e	5

Test 39: Mixed (page 40)

1. **13** The first number decreases by 2.
2. **3** The second number is half the first number, so half of 6 is 3.
3. **28** The second number is double the first number, so 14 x 2 is 28.
4. **44** The first number decreases by 11.
5. **20** The first number increases by 9.
6. **hour** Let's run and catc**h our** bus.
7. **stop** You mu**st op**en all the windows.
8. **land** Pau**l and** Adam liked the film too.
9. **seal** Plea**se al**low enough time to get there.
10. **fern** I definitely pre**fer n**uts to raisins.
11. **sneer** There is only one 'e' in 'corners'.
12. **treat** There is only one 't' in 'feather'.
13. **stand** There is no 'a' in 'dusting'.
14. **slide** There is no 'l' in 'seaside'.
15. **swoon** There is no 's' in 'woodland'.

Test 40: Mixed (page 41)

1. **LAKE**
2. **FURL**
3. **PACK**
4. **BEAT**
5. **FOOL**
6. **SON** lesson
7. **BOW** rainbow
8. **OUT** shouting
9. **ATE** gates
10. **CAR** carpet
11. **VX** Each letter moves forwards four places.
12. **2DX** The number is a repeating pattern: 222222. The first letter moves forward one place. The second letter is a repeating pattern: XXXXXX.
13. **JIL** Each letter moves forward four places.
14. **ghi** This pattern is the alphabet written out in order. It is also an alternating pattern, three letters in lower case, then three letters in capitals, and so on.
15. **9AC** The numbers decrease by 1 each time. The letters move forward four places each time.

EXPANDED ANSWERS

Puzzle 1 (page 42)

In order to do this puzzle, you need to know your compass points.

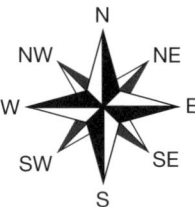

The first instruction asks you to place a X in the NW box. From the compass points, you can see this is the top left box. Proceed in the same manner for all the instructions.

Puzzle 2 (page 42)

With these clock words, the key is to look at the final letter of the given words. For the next word, you are looking for a word that ends in 't'. 'Art' is the only one in the list. Place '-art' after 'd' to give 'dart' and continue in the same way for the other words.

Puzzle 3 (page 43)

1 angle   2 ropes   3 broad
4 cheat   5 spear   6 gable
7 straw   8 peach   9 state
10 table   11 worth   12 stale

Try to solve the puzzle using only Section 1, then Section 2. Section 3 gives you the answers.

Puzzle 4 (page 44)

W wear, wail, whip, wash, when, wall, warm are all words. Be careful with pronunciation, for example, 'ear' and 'wear'. The 'w' changes the sound of 'ear' when put together.
S **soak, scan, star, scar, swan, stow, spit** are all words.
F **fate, fill, fair, fits, four** are all words.
R **reel, rail, rate, rear, roar, rice, rash** are all words.

Puzzle 5 (page 44)

1 CHIEF = CE**F**HI   SQUIRT = IQ**R**STU
   BABY = AB**B**Y   BANANA = AA**A**BNN
   UGLY = GL**U**Y   BETTER = BE**E**RTT
   ZANY = AN**Y**Z   STAIR = AI**R**ST
2 DANGER = AD**E**GNR   BADGE = AB**D**EG
   BABBLE = AB**B**BEL   PORTS = OP**R**ST
   SUMMER = EM**M**RSU   ESCAPE = AC**E**EPS
   BACON = AB**C**NO   EAGLES = AE**E**GLS
1 **February** The third letters of the nonsense words are: F, B, U, Y, R, A, E, R.
2 **December** The third letters of the nonsense words are: E, B, M, C, D, R, E, E.

Bond VR 10 Minute Tests 8–9 years

TEST 24: Mixed

Underline the two words, one from each group, which are the most opposite in meaning.

Example (dawn, <u>early</u>, wake) (<u>late</u>, stop, sunrise)

1. (sleep, lie, work) (night, snore, truth)
2. (backwards, down, beside) (forwards, inside, across)
3. (moon, light, dawn) (day, dusk, night)
4. (talk, broad, tall) (chatter, wide, narrow)
5. (far, steady, closed) (distant, near, firm)

If q = 2, r = 3, s = 5 and t = 10, find the value of:

6. (r + t) − s = _____
7. 6q = _____
8. q + r + s + t = _____

Now give the answers of these calculations as letters:

9. sq = _____
10. q + r + s = _____

Underline the word in each line which uses only letters from the first 12 letters of the alphabet. The alphabet has been written out to help you.

A B C D E F G H I J K L M N O P Q R S T U V W X Y Z

11	basket	lettuce	flannel	chief
12	labelled	bridge	chimney	fussy
13	dragon	decide	flavour	current
14	bitten	joker	dabble	laugh
15	lantern	casket	jackal	height

TEST 25: **Mixed**

Test time: 0 — 5 — 10 minutes

Underline the two words which are made from the same letters.

Example	TAP	PET	<u>TEA</u>	POT	<u>EAT</u>
1	LAP	PAW	PAL	SAP	SAW
2	CARD	DRAW	CROW	WARD	WORD
3	FAT	TAR	FAR	APT	TAP
4	LEFT	FLED	FELT	FEED	DEFT
5	DREAD	BEARD	TREAT	TRADE	BREAD

Look at the first group of three words. The word in the middle has been made from the other two words. Complete the second group of three words in the same way, making a new word in the middle.

Example	PA<u>IN</u>	<u>INTO</u>	<u>TOO</u>K	ALSO	_SOON_	ONLY
6	DENT	DESK	SKIP	BEAN	_____	ARCH
7	FELT	FOOT	BOOK	PEAR	_____	SOOT
8	LIFE	LIPS	TAPS	PILE	_____	EYES
9	GIFT	GIVE	VEST	WISH	_____	DEFY
10	MILK	MOON	SOON	HIGH	_____	LAZY

Complete the following sentences in the best way by choosing one word from each set of brackets.

Example   Tall is to (tree, <u>short</u>, colour) as narrow is to (thin, white, <u>wide</u>).

11   Inside is to (house, garden, outside) as over is to (above, under, near).

12   Big is to (elephant, large, tiny) as small is to (little, pain, quick).

13   Hair is to (head, ribbon, long) as nail is to (wood, hammer, finger).

14   Ink is to (pencil, word, pen) as paint is to (brush, colour, red).

15   Slippery is to (eel, firm, mud) as bumpy is to (smooth, road, track).

Total

TEST 26: **Mixed**

Test time: 0 — 5 — 10 minutes

Underline the word in the brackets closest in meaning to the word in capitals.

Example   UNHAPPY   (unkind   death   laughter   <u>sad</u>   friendly)

1 STRANGE   (ordinary   usual   extra   visitor   peculiar)
2 VEX   (tired   annoy   please   wonder   chew)
3 STRAIGHT   (curved   narrow   direct   lined   crooked)
4 PEEP   (peck   glide   stare   horn   glance)
5 TIP   (pour   catch   money   bottom   bin)

Find the four-letter word hidden at the end of one word and the beginning of the next word. The order of the letters may not be changed.

Example   The children had bat<u>s and</u> balls.   ___sand___

6 Please take those coats off our chairs.   _____
7 Ravi is so quick, he will win every race.   _____
8 Sarah ate a whole tin of toffees.   _____
9 One star is shining particularly brightly.   _____
10 Leaves are blowing in the air in the yard.   _____

Remove one letter from the word in capitals to leave a new word. The meaning of the new word is given in the clue.

Example   AUNT   an insect   ___ant___

11 THANK   container   _____
12 TANGLE   corner   _____
13 SWARM   bathed   _____
14 SLIGHT   vision   _____
15 STEEP   tread   _____

27

Total

TEST 27: **Mixed**

Test time: 0 — 5 — 10 minutes

Change the first word into the last word, by changing one letter at a time and making a new, different word in the middle.

Example   CASE   _CASH_   LASH

1 WINE   _____   MINT
2 SLIT   _____   SLOW
3 WASH   _____   BATH
4 RUNG   _____   LONG
5 BEST   _____   BOAT

Underline the two words which are the odd ones out in the following groups of words.

Example   black   <u>king</u>   purple   green   <u>house</u>

6 respect   garden   value   prize   letter
7 square   rectangle   hexagon   oval   circle
8 one   two   third   fourth   fifth
9 cost   expense   money   shop   price
10 dark   light   flimsy   delicate   tough

Find the missing number by using the two numbers outside the brackets in the same way as the other sets of numbers.

Example   2 [8] 4   3 [18] 6   5 [25] 5

11 16 [14] 2   24 [12] 12   18 [__] 6
12 20 [5] 4   10 [2] 5   8 [__] 8
13 3 [7] 4   5 [13] 8   4 [__] 7
14 5 [25] 5   4 [16] 4   3 [__] 3
15 8 [2] 4   12 [3] 4   12 [__] 6

TEST 28: **Mixed**

Test time: 0 5 10 minutes

Fill in the missing letters and numbers.
The alphabet has been written out to help you.
A B C D E F G H I J K L M N O P Q R S T U V W X Y Z

Example   AB is to CD as PQ is to _RS_.

1 MO is to PR as SU is to ____.

2 19D is to 17E as 15F is to ____.

3 ML is to KJ as ED is to ____.

4 A1B is to C2D as E3F is to ____.

5 nop is to qrs as tuv is to ____.

Which one letter can be added to the front of all these words to make new words?

Example   _c_ are   _c_ at   _c_ rate   _c_ all

6 ___ arm   ___ attest   ___ ox   ___ ling
7 ___ rain   ___ right   ___ last   ___ lank
8 ___ ape   ___ ought   ___ ail   ___ ice
9 ___ ager   ___ mpty   ___ at   ___ yes
10 ___ limb   ___ rust   ___ rash   ___ lock

Underline the two words, one from each group, that are closest in meaning.

Example   (race, shop, <u>start</u>)   (finish, <u>begin</u>, end)

11 (lift, choose, cling)   (raise, drop, fall)
12 (know, path, wander)   (wonder, stray, run)
13 (few, weird, even)   (normal, odd, many)
14 (furry, hairless, muddy)   (clean, tiny, hairy)
15 (sight, fight, might)   (battle, hearing, claim)

TEST 29: **Mixed**

Test time: 0 — 5 — 10 minutes

These words have been written in code but the codes are not under the correct words. Match each word to the correct code.

| MILK | FILM | LAMB | LIMP |
| QXHR | QPHZ | CPQH | HPQJ |

1 MILK _____   2 FILM _____

3 LAMB _____   4 LIMP _____

Using the same code, decode:

5 RXQQ _____

Underline the pair of words most similar in meaning.

Example   come, go   <u>roam, wander</u>   fear, fare

6   pick, mix   forgive, forget   peel, skin
7   reply, respond   question, answer   ask, shout
8   laugh, cry   weeping, smiling   giggle, chuckle
9   collect, deliver take, away   gather, assemble
10 entrance, exit   entire, complete   play, ground

Change the first word of the third pair in the same way as the other pairs to give a new word.

Example   bind, hind   bare, hare   but, _hut_

11 comb, coming   town, towing   bore, _____
12 rust, rush   crust, crush   bust, _____
13 nuts, stun   drab, bard   flow, _____
14 loin, lion   silt, slit   form, _____
15 pillow, pill   milked, milk   starts, _____

TEST 30: **Mixed**

Test time: 0 — 5 — 10 minutes

If v = 3, w = 8, y = 5 and z = 7, find the value of:

1 vw − y = _____
2 2y + z = _____
3 3z − 3v = _____
4 w + y + z = _____
5 w − y = _____

Find the three-letter word which can be added to the letters in capitals to make a new word. The new word will complete the sentence sensibly.

Example   The cat sprang onto the MO.   __USE__

6 Put them on the table over RE please.   _____
7 Simon is the postman who delivers letters and PELS in our street.   _____
8 Our teacher likes us to S the door quietly, not slam it.   _____
9 The children SPLED merrily in the puddles.   _____
10 The old man sits in his favourite ARMCH by the fire.   _____

Add one letter to the word given in capital letters to make a new word. The meaning of the new word is given in the clue.

Example   PLAN   simple   __plain__

11 TEN   a cloth shelter   _____
12 WAS   an insect   _____
13 FIST   before second   _____
14 PLAN   not patterned   _____
15 STEP   high and sloping   _____

TEST 31: Mixed

If the code for MARKET is 547932, what are the codes for the following words?

1. MAKE — 5493
2. TRAM — 2745
3. TAME — 2453

Using the same code, decode:

4. 2345 — TEAM
5. 5423 — MATE

Choose the word or phrase that makes each sentence true.

Example   A LIBRARY always has (posters, carpets, <u>books</u>, DVDs, stairs).

6. A BEETLE always has (<u>legs</u>, stripes, food, shelter, spots).
7. A BED always has (a duvet, pillows, pyjamas, <u>a mattress</u>, sheets).
8. A BOOK always has (a story, pictures, a bookshelf, a library, <u>pages</u>).
9. A CAR always has (a driver, passengers, a boot, <u>wheels</u>, four doors).
10. A GROCERY SHOP always has (a restaurant, clothes, <u>food</u>, flowers, a bakery).

Look at the first group of three words. The word in the middle has been made from the other two words. Complete the second group of three words in the same way, making a new word in the middle.

Example   PAIN   INTO   TOOK   ALSO   <u>SOON</u>   ONLY

11. BELT   BEAN   ANTS   PICK   PILE   LEAN
12. QUIP   QUAY   BRAY   FLEW   FLAP   SWAP
13. JAMS   JOIN   COIN   WEST   WADE   FADE
14. SPUN   SOON   WOOL   FAIL   FOOL   TOOK
15. KING   KILT   SALT   MILK   MICE   FACE

Test 32: Mixed

Find the letter which will end the first word and start the second word.

Example   peac (h) ome

1 pat (___) ope
2 bel (___) han
3 her (___) nce
4 cla (___) ise
5 bac (___) ite

Find the four-letter word hidden at the end of one word and the beginning of the next word. The order of the letters may not be changed.

Example   The children had bat<u>s and</u> balls.   _sand_

6 All of us caught our balls.   _____
7 The waves tossed the boat.   _____
8 The old car door was very rusty.   _____
9 The horse jumped over the fence.   _____
10 Both animals were extremely fierce.   _____

Underline the one word which cannot be made from the letters of the word in capital letters.

Example	STATIONERY	stones	tyres	ration	<u>nation</u>	noisy
11	THINKING	grin	king	thin	ink	hint
12	BATTLES	slate	bats	steal	blade	bleat
13	CUSHION	such	nose	coin	shun	chin
14	BIRTHDAY	dirt	yard	drab	bath	drain
15	HISTORY	story	shirt	roast	hoist	rosy

Time for a break! Go to Puzzle Page 44

Test 33: Mixed

Fill in the crosswords so that all the given words are included.
You have been given one letter as a clue in each crossword.

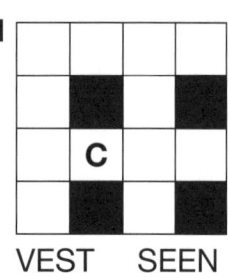
VEST SEEN
VAIN ICED

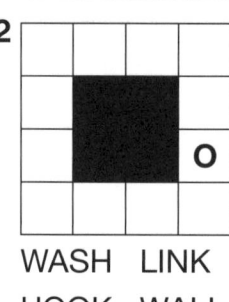
WASH LINK
HOOK WALL

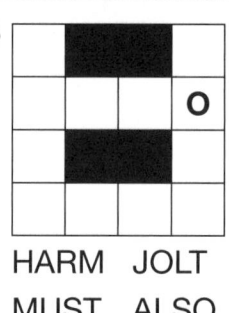
HARM JOLT
MUST ALSO

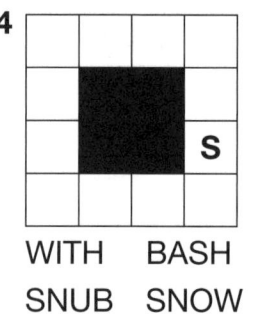
WITH BASH
SNUB SNOW

Some children have after school activities.

Child A has ballet on Monday, dancing on Thursday and tennis on Saturday. Child B has scouts on Wednesday and football on Sunday. Child C has ballet on Monday, art on Tuesday, music on Thursday and athletics on Saturday. Child D has swimming on Monday, scouts on Wednesday and football on Sunday. Child E has swimming on Monday, dancing on Thursday and tennis on Saturday.

5 How many children play football? _____
6 Which activity takes place on Tuesday? _____
7 On which day is there no activity? _____
8 Which child has the most activities? _____
9 Which child has Mondays free but is busy on Sundays? _____
10 Which child does activities that none of the others do? _____

Complete the following sentences in the best way by choosing one word from each set of brackets.

Example   Tall is to (tree, <u>short</u>, colour) as narrow is to (thin, white, <u>wide</u>).

11 Chew is to (food, swallow, munch) as talk is to (phone, eat, chat).
12 February is to (winter, month, year) as Sunday is to (weekend, day, holiday).
13 War is to (peace, battle, fight) as sadness is to (happiness, rain, darkness).
14 Pillow is to (cushion, bed, feather) as rug is to (room, picture, mat).
15 Cat is to (whiskers, tail, 4 legs) as man is to (woman, 2 legs, arms).

TEST 34: **Mixed**

Test time: 0 — 5 — 10 minutes

Fill in the missing numbers and letters in each sequence.

Example	2	4	6	8	10	_12_
1	7	____	15	19	23	27
2	31	42	53	64	____	86
3	2	4	____	16	32	64
4	21	16	12	____	7	6
5	____	13x	16w	19v	22u	25t

Underline the two words which are the odd ones out in the following groups of words.

Example	black	<u>king</u>	purple	green	<u>house</u>
6	Wales	Leeds	London	Scotland	Ireland
7	right	left	fair	honest	dark
8	candle	lamp	torch	cloud	basin
9	mirror	newspaper	book	picture	magazine
10	son	daughter	grandfather	nephew	mother

Underline the word in the brackets closest in meaning to the word in capital letters.

Example	UNHAPPY	(unkind	death	laughter	<u>sad</u>	friendly)
11	TIMID	(nervous	bold	quick	expensive	brave)
12	MAIN	(water	chief	stay	part	pony)
13	UNDER	(over	beside	beneath	inside	outside)
14	VARIABLE	(plain	constant	coloured	changeable	fixed)
15	SINGE	(tuneful	carol	warm	beat	burn)

Total

Test 35: Mixed

Underline the two words which are made from the same letters.

Example   TAP   PET   <u>TEA</u>   POT   <u>EAT</u>

1   RAP   APE   PAT   PEA   TAR
2   NAIL   RAIN   LAIR   HAIR   RAIL
3   REAR   RAIN   NEAR   REAL   RARE
4   NET   ITS   TIN   SIT   SET
5   TASTE   TREAT   STATE   TOAST   TEASE

Fill in the crosswords so that all the given words are included. You have been given one letter as a clue in each crossword.

6
DESK   STEW
EDIT   KNOW

7
SOME   JAMS
JAZZ   ZOOM

8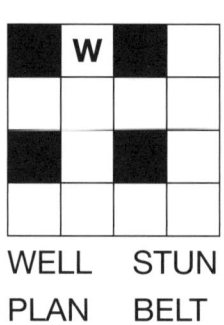
WELL   STUN
PLAN   BELT

9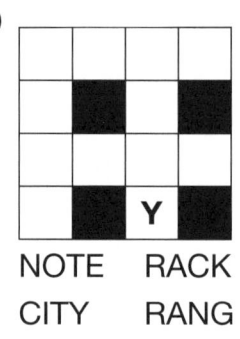
NOTE   RACK
CITY   RANG

Complete the following sentences by selecting the most sensible word from each group of words given in the brackets. Underline the words selected.

Example   The (<u>children</u>, books, foxes) carried the (houses, <u>books</u>, steps) home from the (greengrocer, <u>library</u>, factory).

10   Kieran skilfully (called, controlled, kissed) the ball and (passed, flew, pierced) it to Marek who scored a (look, goal, pigeon).

11   'Why can't you (listen, eat, climb) carefully to (table, instructions, pebbles)?' (shouted, dug, swam) Dad.

12   It is said (than, think, that) only one tenth of an (ice cream, icicle, iceberg) is visible above the (fire, earth, water) surface level.

13   Some (classrooms, sheep, jackets) have (horns, waterfalls, fences) but many do (knot, no, not).

14   When I had (started, wished, finished) (writing, eating, playing) my story, I went out to (cry, play, work).

15   At (school, hospital, pavement) we are (learning, eating, shouting) about the Romans and their way of (school, life, help) in Britain.

TEST 36: **Mixed**

Test time: 0 — 5 — 10 minutes

Find the three-letter word which can be added to the letters in capitals to make a new word. The new word will complete the sentence sensibly.

Example   The cat sprang onto the MO.   __USE__

1 Please sit D on that chair.   _____
2 He has a kind face with big brown E.   _____
3 Your GDMOTHER is taller than mine.   _____
4 Driving on the motorway to London takes about half an H.   _____
5 Gina's cat has just had KITS.   _____

The chart below shows how many pets two classes have.

	DOGS	CATS	FISH	GERBILS	OTHERS	NONE
CLASS X	3	12	3	2	7	2
CLASS Y	7	9	6	0	11	3

6 Which pet is most popular of all?   _____
7 Which pet is more popular in Class Y, dogs or fish?   _____
8 How many children altogether have no pets?   _____
9 Which column has the greatest number in Class Y?   _____
10 Which pet is twice as popular in Class Y than Class X?   _____
11 How many gerbils and 'other' pets are owned by both classes?   _____

Underline two words, one from each group, that go together to form a new word. The word in the first group always comes first.

Example   (hand, <u>green</u>, for)   (light, <u>house</u>, sure)

12 (orange, bath, bubble)   (soap, sky, room)
13 (off, soft, bit)   (ten, win, bed)
14 (know, term, win)   (rim, ledge, side)
15 (slippery, quick, stony)   (rock, change, sand)

37

Total

TEST 37: **Mixed**

Test time: 0　　5　　10 minutes

Fill in the crosswords so that all the given words are included.
You have been given one letter as a clue in each crossword.

| 1 | 2 | 3 | 4 |

ZERO　ECHO　　GIFT　REEF　　PLAY　COSY　　TIDE　LAME
CAKE　ACHE　　WING　WORK　　BELL　VETO　　FLAT　FURL

The houses on one side of a street are even numbers from 2 to 20.
On the other side they are odd numbers from 1 to 19.
1 is opposite 2, 3 is opposite 4 and so on.

5　What number house is opposite 7?　_____

6　What number house is opposite 14?　_____

7　What number house is a higher number and next to 17?　_____

8　Which house is a lower number and opposite to 10?　_____

House number 3 and House number 4 have blue doors.
House number 4 and House number 5 have window boxes.
House number 3 and House number 6 have large door knockers.
Houses 5 and 6 have green doors.
Which house has:

9　a green door and a large door knocker?　_____
10　a blue door and a window box?　_____

Look at these groups of words.
Group A: ON LAND　　Group B: ON WATER　　Group C: IN THE AIR
Choose the correct group for each of the types of transport below.
Write in the letter.

11　boat　_____　　12　train　_____
13　ship　_____　　14　van　_____
15　helicopter　_____

TEST 38: **Mixed**

Test time: 0 — 5 — 10 minutes

Which one letter can be added to the front of all these words to make new words?

Example   _c_ are   _c_ at   _c_ rate   _c_ all

1 ___ eel   ___ earth   ___ eat   ___ and
2 ___ ram   ___ lease   ___ ink   ___ itch
3 ___ evil   ___ ear   ___ ark   ___ rink
4 ___ port   ___ weep   ___ team   ___ tray
5 ___ nit   ___ ill   ___ not   ___ night

Underline the pair of words most similar in meaning.

Example   come, go   <u>roam, wander</u>   fear, fare

6   tall, thin   high, low   breadth, width
7   look, listen   save, conserve   rash, sensible
8   tint, hue   blue, colour   sky, sea
9   tie, laces   bind, weed   knot, fasten
10 soft, touch   smooth, silky   delicate, harsh

If these words were placed in alphabetical order, which would come second to last? Underline the word.

11 talk   converse shout   yell   call
12 high   low   below   above   up
13 biscuit cake   sandwich cookie   tart
14 screw   nail   tack   pin   hammer
15 light   dark   night   day   sunshine

TEST 39: **Mixed**

Test time: 0 — 5 — 10 minutes

Underline the number that completes each sequence.

1. 21 is to 19 as 15 is to (13, 17, 11).
2. 8 is to 4 as 6 is to (12, 3, 18).
3. 13 is to 26 as 14 is to (27, 28, 18).
4. 77 is to 66 as 55 is to (44, 555, 11).
5. 1 is to 10 as 11 is to (16, 20, 2).

Find the four-letter word hidden at the end of one word and the beginning of the next word. The order of the letters may not be changed.

Example   The children had bat<u>s and</u> balls.   _sand_

6. Let's run and catch our bus.   _____
7. You must open all the windows.   _____
8. Paul and Adam liked the film too.   _____
9. Please allow enough time to get there.   _____
10. I definitely prefer nuts to raisins.   _____

Underline the one word which cannot be made from the letters of the word in capital letters.

Example	STATIONERY	stones	tyres	ration	<u>nation</u>	noisy
11	CORNERS	crone	rose	snore	sneer	corn
12	FEATHER	there	reef	treat	fear	heart
13	DUSTING	stand	gust	stud	sting	sung
14	SEASIDE	seed	slide	aside	dies	ease
15	WOODLAND	wool	load	wand	lawn	swoon

TEST 40: **Mixed**

Test time: 0 5 10 minutes

Change the first word into the last word, by changing one letter at a time and making a new, different word in the middle.

Example	CASE	__CASH__	LASH
1	WAKE	_____	LAME
2	HURL	_____	FURY
3	PICK	_____	BACK
4	FEAT	_____	BOAT
5	TOOL	_____	FOAL

Find the three-letter word which can be added to the letters in capitals to make a new word. The new word will complete the sentence sensibly.

Example   The cat sprang onto the MO.   __USE__

6 In our Music LES today, we played guitars.   _____

7 Look at the beautiful RAIN arching across the sky!   _____

8 Talking very loudly is called SHING.   _____

9 In the countryside you must close GS to fields behind you.   _____

10 Mrs Newman has a new PET in her sitting room.   _____

Give the missing groups of letters and numbers in the following sequences. The alphabet has been written out to help you.

A B C D E F G H I J K L M N O P Q R S T U V W X Y Z

Example	CQ	DP	EQ	FP	GQ	__HP__
11	BD	FH	JL	NP	RT	____
12	2AX	2BX	2CX	____	2EX	2FX
13	BAD	FEH	____	NMP	RQT	VUX
14	abc	DEF	____	JKL	mno	PQR
15	____	8EG	7IK	6MO	5QS	4UW

Time for a break! Go to Puzzle Page 44

Total

Puzzle 1

Noughts and Crosses

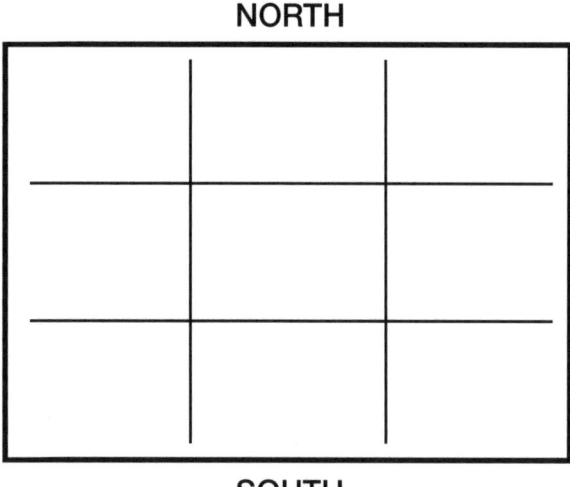

Follow the instructions using the compass points, and place the Os and ×s in the correct places. Draw a line to show who wins the game by getting three of their symbols in a row.

1 × in the NW box.
2 O in the SE box.
3 × in the SW box.
4 O in the W box.
5 × in the NE box.
6 O in the centre.
7 × in the N box.

Puzzle 2

Clock Words

Here is an unusual clock! Each of the numbers has been replaced by a letter.

Start at '12 o'clock' and go round the letters making words back up to the w at the top.

As you work your way round the clock, each missing word begins and ends with one of the letters in the squares. The missing words are shown in the body of the clock. The first one has been done for you.

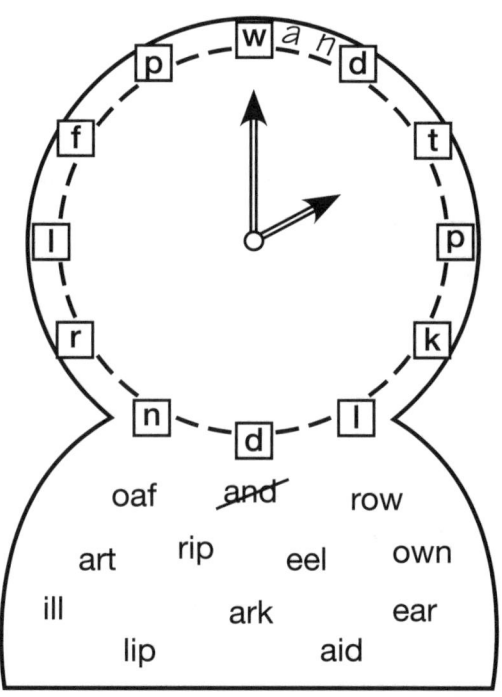

Puzzle 3

Arranging Anagrams

The letters of the following words can be rearranged to make different words.

There are 3 sections to this puzzle. First try to solve the anagram by looking at Section 1. To check your answer, look at the clues in Section 2. If you still can't solve it, in Section 3 you will find the word in a mixed list.

SECTION 1

1	angel	_angle_
2	spore	_____
3	board	_____
4	teach	_____
5	reaps	_____
6	bagel	_____
7	warts	_____
8	cheap	_____
9	taste	_____
10	bleat	_____
11	throw	_____
12	least	_____

SECTION 2

1	a corner
2	cords, bonds
3	wide, not narrow
4	to swindle
5	a weapon you throw
6	the end of a building
7	animal bedding
8	a juicy fruit
9	USA is divided into 50 of these
10	you eat on it, sitting on a chair
11	value
12	not fresh

SECTION 3

~~angle~~	gable	ropes	spear
table	straw	state	peach
cheat	worth	stale	broad

Puzzle 4

Word Wall

Shade the bricks that make a word that starts with the letter in bold. Each letter in bold uses two bars. Here is an example.

B	OLD	ASH	FIN	OWN
	ARM	ALL	EAR	END

W	EAR	AIL	TOP	HIP	ASH
	BID	HEN	ALL	ARM	KIT
S	OAK	JAR	CAN	TAR	CAR
	WAN	TOW	PIT	ALL	OWL
F	ATE	ILL	ASH	ITS	OUR
	OAR	ICE	AIR	FOX	MOW
R	EEL	HOP	AIL	ATE	EAR
	OAR	ICE	ASH	SEA	MOW

Puzzle 5

Alphabet Scramble

Put the letters of each of these words into alphabetical order.

1.
CHIEF	_____	SQUIRT	_____
BABY	_____	BANANA	_____
UGLY	_____	BETTER	_____
ZANY	_____	STAIR	_____

2.
DANGER	_____	BADGE	_____
BABBLE	_____	PORTS	_____
SUMMER	_____	ESCAPE	_____
BACON	_____	EAGLES	_____

Now take the third letter of each of your new nonsense words and rearrange them to spell out two months of the year.

1 _____   2 _____

Progress Grid

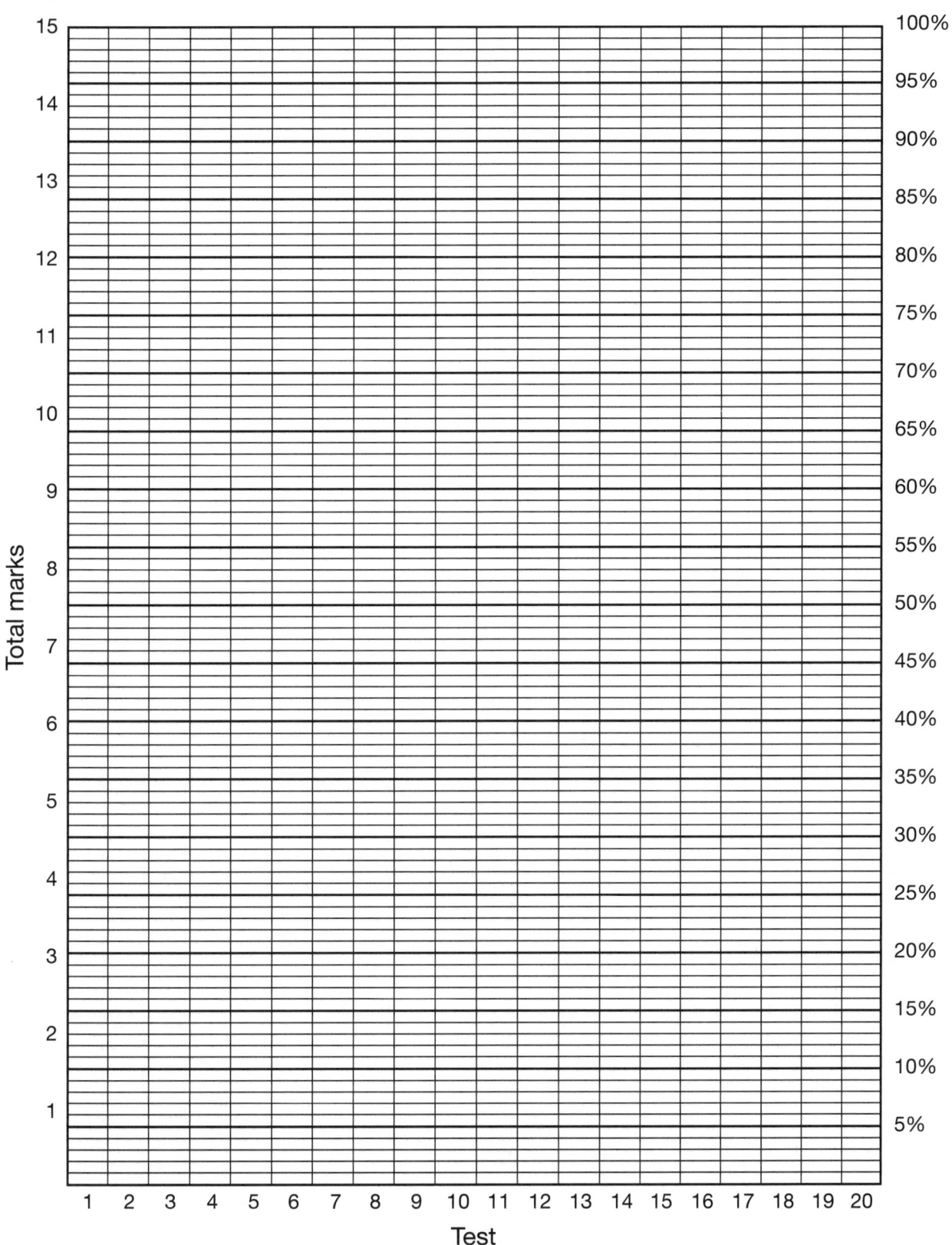

Progress Grid

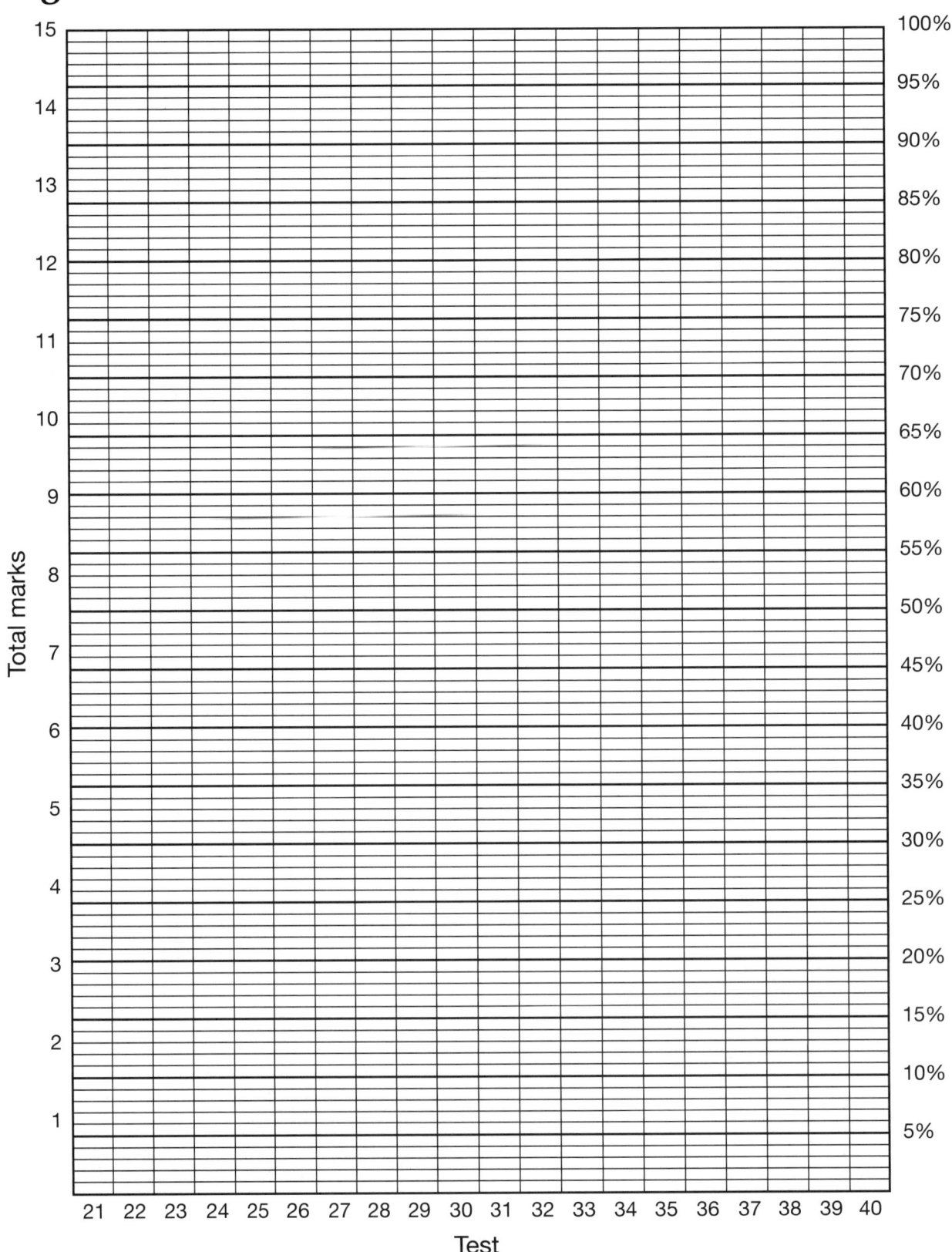